BOOST YOU
BRAIN P

Essential advice on how to become the successful parent of a successful child, dealing with all the facts involved, but with the emphasis on good nutrition based on the author's well-publicized and revealing nutritional trial with second-year schoolchildren at Darland High School, a large comprehensive school in North Wales.

BOOST YOUR CHILD'S BRAIN POWER

How to use good nutrition to ensure success at school

by
Gwilym Roberts

THORSONS PUBLISHING GROUP

First published 1988

© Gwilym Roberts 1988

British Library Cataloguing in Publication Data

Roberts, Gwilym
Boost your child's brain power: how to
use good nutrition to ensure success at
school.
1. Children. Nutrition — For parents
I. Title
613.2'088054

ISBN 0-7225-1752-1

Published by Thorsons Publishers Limited,
Wellingborough, Northamptonshire, NN8 2RQ, England

Printed in Great Britain by Biddles Limited, Guildford, Surrey

3   5   7   9   10   8   6   4   2

DEDICATION

To Bethan, Rhian and Eifion

CONTENTS

PART V: PROBLEMS IN AND OUT OF SCHOOL

ACKNOWLEDGEMENT

To my darling wife Myfi, who has made bringing up our three children a joy, and whose help in writing this book has been indispensable.

PREFACE

This book is written for parents who want the best for their children; it is for all those parents who want their children to do as well as they possibly can in every area of school life, and who wish them to take their place in society as healthy, happy, confident, secure, popular and successful individuals.

As a parent of three children in their twenties, and, as a teacher of twenty-eight years experience, I know the kind of problems that parents face and the kind of information and help needed to resolve these problems. When people claim that it's not easy bringing up children in today's society, that must be the understatement of the century.

This book will give parents a new hope, a new optimism, and, more importantly, a new confidence to embark on the exciting, enjoyable and unpredictable task of providing their children with an education which can be both stimulating and meaningful, and also with a means of developing in their children attitudes and personalities that will make them acceptable and successful when they become adults.

My book is the result of many years dedicated to the education of school children and to the understanding of their individual needs. It is also the result, in the past few years, of the study of correct nutritional practices in relation to growing and maturing children. This combination of the educational and the nutritional, with elements of philosophy, psychology and school know-how, is the recipe for your child's success. It is a recipe that is bound to produce phenomenal results. Try it.

INTRODUCTION

Would you like to see your child behaving better, doing better at school, being able to enjoy life and being well-adjusted enough to cope with all the stresses and temptations of today's society?

Of course you would, and that is why, for your son or daughter, and certainly for yourself, this book is the most important investment you have ever made.

It will show you how to become the successful parent of a successful child. It will give you the know-how and confidence to tackle the problems you will most certainly encounter with your youngsters, and will lead ultimately to a tremendous sense of achievement, satisfaction and pride.

If your child is not doing quite as well, or maybe nowhere near as well as you expect, if their behaviour and performance at school are just about passable and acceptable, but you feel that they are capable of far better things, what might be the reason, and who gets the blame?

The family has always been a convenient scapegoat. Poor toilet training, a lack of breastfeeding, being picked up too often or left to cry are all offered as reasons for later bad behaviour.

No one would blame you for thinking this way. We've been led since Victorian times to think that there must be some Freudian explanation for any sort of problem or failure, and that some form of past experience has put paid to any hope of normal development and progress.

It is also true that life today is getting more and more difficult for youngsters. More of their parents are divorcing or separating than ever before, some of them may join a 'new' family created by re-marrying and increase further the stress they face. There is more pressure on them to smoke, drink, find a girl/boy friend at an early age, question their parents' judgements and ideals and experiment with drugs. They see so much violence on television, fact and fiction, that it is a wonder any of them are remotely well adjusted.

Of course all this is extremely worrying, but most problems do have a solution, and there are ways of tackling even the most formidable ones. There can be no single cause of misbehaviour, or failure to learn, and when you have a real understanding of your youngster's type, personality, needs and enormous potential, such things will become exciting challenges rather than formidable barriers.

What this book is about is ALL the facets which are likely to, and undoubtedly do, affect your child's development into the talented, successful adult they can be. And I stress again, the ALL, because there can never be just a single factor – we are not going to treat things in isolation in this book, but will be dealing with the whole child.

Perhaps your child's performance or behaviour at school has been so disturbing that you've had to seek counselling in one form or another. You may have had a discussion with the Headmaster or House Tutor, or perhaps you've been offered the services of the Educational Psychologist which are available at every State school.

I've seen many well-meaning counselling and psychological probings being performed in schools, and I'm afraid to say, with very little real success. They've not often considered the whole child and the overall management of this unique and individual being.

So you might well ask, have parents, teachers, psychiatrists, doctors, ministers and all manner of paediatricians been on the wrong track? They have to a great extent. Neither have books which deal with learning and behavioural problems had it right completely either. They have not appreciated or identified the need to consider every dimension of the child's makeup and needs.

Consequently, what's happened is that we're sinking deeper and deeper into an ignorance of how we really need to deal with our youngsters, at a time when they desperately need guidance.

I know I can help you develop a successful and well adjusted child, who will be a delight to you and your family.

Let me tell you then what's wrong with our handling of our children, wrong with our handling of the boy who is a problem learner in the lowest class, and wrong with the girl who gets top marks and an excellent report. Both extremes have such a vast capacity for improvement, something very few people have really appreciated, that this book is for the child who wins at everything just as much as it is for the one who struggles at everything. The child who seems an abysmal failure can start winning, and the constant winner can start to achieve more and more, with greater pleasure and with increased confidence.

Part I
BRAINPOWER

Chapter 1.
The million times potential

Chapter 2.
The pressures on your child

Chapter 3.
Identifying and controlling stress

CHAPTER 1
THE MILLION TIMES
POTENTIAL

Supposing you were suddenly to hear, over the radio, the voice of one of your favourite film stars. What would you be reminded of? Think about what actually happened to make these recollections flow. Just hearing that familiar voice will have triggered off an amazingly complicated process, resulting in a flood of thoughts, memories and emotions created by their films – a process infinitely more complex and sophisticated than the most modern of up-to-date computers.

You are not going to take these highly complicated procedures for granted any more. I want you to think very seriously about the tremendous capabilities and potential of the brain and then you will realise what is possible for your child to accomplish.

The brain is, of course, by far the most important organ of the body, that mass of nerve tissue which controls all body functions, regulates our breathing, our heart beat and our digestion, to mention only a few of its many functions.

The outer layer of the brain is the CORTEX, which contains billions of nerve cells called Neurons. These are the receivers and senders of tiny electrical impulses, which stimulate and establish pathways through which we are able to perform sophisticated tasks of thinking, remembering, understanding, interpreting, evaluating and reasoning.

This two pound or so of grey matter that your child carries around is only about one-fiftieth of their total body weight, but it is where all thought processes, decisions and learning occur. This wonderful, underestimated, little-understood master organ of the body has a million times more potential in your child than you or anyone else have ever imagined.

This director of all operations and activities in the body is grossly neglected and ignored by most people. Dr David Samuels of the Wiseman Institute in America has estimated that from one hundred thousand to one million chemical reactions take place in the brain – no, not in the brain of an Einstein, but in the 'ordinary' brain of your 'ordinary' child.

Although we are still far from a real and comprehensive understanding of how the brain works, it is important to have some idea of what goes on. In a very simplified manner, this is what happens.

The brain communicates with the rest of the body through two main systems – the nerves themselves, and the bloodstream. The nervous system stems from the brain and from the spinal cord, which carries the nerve fibres to all parts of the body, so that, at any instant, impulses can be transmitted to the brain either from stimuli within the body or from the outside environment. Information about the environment reaches the brain via the sensory apparatus – our eyes, ears, nose, taste, and sense of touch – and this is what we call perception. The brain also receives essential information from within the body, from muscles, bones, joints, organs and tissues.

Consider what happens when we pick up a very hot object unexpectedly: an impulse is sent through the nerves from the hand to the brain. The brain deciphers the message and reacts by sending an outgoing or effector impulse back to the muscles of the hand and fingers, and these respond instantaneously. The speed with which we pick up and then drop a hot object reflects how very rapid is this double action, to the brain and back.

People are programmed by all the events and experiences which they have encountered in their lives, and all of these experiences form individual pathways in the brain where they are stored. When you watch a film, the sensory nerves will be stimulated by all sorts of things peculiar to that film, and every impulse to the brain will establish a pathway or memory which is securely stored until needed. Any of these memories can easily be triggered off by all sorts of things – something you see, something you hear. Again, despite its complexity, the process takes place at lightning speed and illustrates just one minute aspect of the power of the human brain.

This fantastic brain, then, the seat of all learning and behaviour, is the organ that you, as a powerful force behind your child, must understand and respect. Have you ever read a book that's praised your child's amazingly wonderful brain and told you how to look after it and develop it? Have you ever taken your child to a doctor who's commented with rapture on his marvellous thought processes and told you how to make them more efficient still? Have you yourself thought how fantastic it is that your child can feel emotions which can sometimes make them laugh or cry; that they can recognize you in a crowd of very similar people; that they can convey to you likes and dislikes, wants and worries?

Most important of all, have you ever thought about the perfectly feasible prospect of developing your child's brain into a really 'super' brain? If not, do you know how to go about it?

You may have read other informative books about children:- about the process of birth; feeding a baby; sleep problems; table manners; milestones in development and so on. However, not many books will venture further than childhood and the junior years, because, at this stage, things get more complicated. There are few books that will explore the realms of behaviour and learning among older children, in a language that all parents can understand. Fewer books will provide solutions to the problems of behaviour and learning in the older child.

With this book you will have at your disposal all the information you need in order to stimulate and protect your child's wonderful brain. Even if you've neglected the appropriate stimuli for establishing good learning habits during early childhood, you've still got plenty of time to make up any omissions. Bear in mind that the brain's development is not complete until a child is seventeen years of age.

So, what we must do, is identify the factors which stimulate and encourage this complex and sensitive brain to develop, and at the same time take action to avoid the factors that will disturb its fine balance and prevent it from functioning optimally.

1. Firstly, your child's brain will not function efficiently unless you provide it with proper nutrition. It is very

sensitive to a shortage of nutrients and oxygen, and no amount of protection or stimulation will compensate for an inadequate diet.

2. Secondly, your child's brain will need to be stimulated in a way that will suit your child's individual need. The important fact to bear in mind is that all children are different and their needs will vary.

3. Thirdly, the brain is very sensitive to our twentieth century environment. There are many pollutants and poisons in the air and in the soil which affect the function of the brain. The most serious of these dangers to the brain is lead, most of which comes from car exhausts and can easily reach the brain once it is inside the body. There are simple precautions you can take to avoid this possibility, and to neutralize the harmful effect of these pollutants.

4. Lastly, and most importantly, you must protect your child's brain from that scourge of modern life –

Stress

In the next chapters, I shall explain to you, step by step, how to nourish, stimulate and protect the brain, so that it becomes the powerful tool that it should be in determining the progress of your youngster through life.

CHAPTER 2
THE PRESSURES ON
YOUR CHILD

Our one-time next-door neighbour couldn't make out why her ten-year-old son Christopher felt sick and 'played up' at lunch time every other Thursday. The family lived near school and Chris came home for lunch every day. The mother couldn't understand why her son was in such a state, on alternate Thursdays only. He always complained of feeling sick before she served lunch, wouldn't eat, whined incessantly and seemed, she said, 'frightened of something'. It took a bit of persuasion to get out of him that he was frightened of going to the Swimming Baths, which his class visited every other week. Chris had never been very confident in water but would go in the sea with his father. In a crowded pool, sharing two adults with a whole class, he felt that something would surely happen to him. His pals tried to help him swim but this frightened him all the more. This kind of fear, the response of the individual to what he thinks is a threatening situation, is called stress. There is a link between stress and illness, stress and unhappiness, stress and under-achievement – for the adult at work and for the child at school.

It's only in the past decade that stress has been recognized as an element in our lives that can wreak havoc unless we learn how to manage it.

What many parents seldom realize is that their children, too, can be under tremendous stress for a great number of reasons, and that they can experience the traumas of stress just as much as an adult can. Children themselves know quite well what stress is, and that it causes unexplained headaches, 'butterflies' and pain in their stomachs, blushing, a dry throat, weak knees, a feeling of panic, and so on.

It is absolutely vital for you to teach your child how to recognize stress and how to handle it once it is recognized. It's easy, and so rewarding once you know how. And it's important for you to be able to handle stress as well, because a parent exhibiting the symptoms of stress will soon transfer this anxiety to a child. Not that all stress is to be avoided. A degree of stress is the impetus that many a child or adult needs to complete a task or get going with some project or activity. It's when stress gets out of hand, when it becomes too difficult to handle, that we're in trouble.

Before we can control stress, we must really understand what it is, and understand what happens to the body and the brain when an adult or child is put under stress.

Most people have ways of dealing with simple anxieties, but we can cope with only a certain number before these anxieties overwhelm us. Today, stress affects everyone, and contributes to a vast number of hospital admissions every year, not to mention the percentage of us who suffer from such 'usual' things as tension headaches, fatigue or mental confusion brought about by the pressures of everyday life, with its traffic jams, job demands, noise, shopping queues, and so on. No-one can be happy under stress. No child can perform well under stress, or learn, or succeed.

The human animal has an automatic built-in mechanism for dealing with stress, and, whatever the type of stress, this mechanism in our body always works in the same way. It hasn't changed since primitive man roamed our land, confronted with threatening and therefore stressful situations. The response of primitive man was 'Fight or Flight', which meant that his body would immediately react in such a way as to be able to attack the enemy who was stealing his food, or threatening his family. The hormones adrenalin and nor-adrenalin would instantly pour into his bloodstream signalling the release of stored glucose to improve his physical and mental agility. His heart would beat faster; his bones released calcium; his pancreas released insulin and the blood vessels constricted. The result was a swift transfer of the quick energy-releasing glucose into the muscle cells to get them ready to put up a fight or beat a hasty retreat.

The snag nowadays is that this body reaction of primitive man to a threatening situation is what happens to modern man – to all of us, adults and children of today. It is the type of threatening situation, the type of stress, that is different and so damaging. Although the response of the body is the same as it ever was, we can't nowadays – not usually anyway – 'fight' or take 'flight'. You can't punch the boss on the nose when he presents you with impossible deadlines and demands. You have to bottle your anger and comply. You can't run if you're in a traffic jam; you sit there, becoming more and more agitated. You can't fight the cost of living, or beaurocracy or the hundreds of rules and regulations that govern our lives.

It is therefore, very difficult to rid the body of the tremendous amount of glucose which is available in the muscles, and difficult to burn off all the other metabolites that adrenalin produces. The whole body chemistry is disrupted and, if this disruption happens on a fairly regularly basis, there is an intolerable strain on the adrenal glands, with the result that, eventually, exhaustion occurs. The immune system that protects the body from ailments and diseases will be weakened as well; the white blood cells will become defective and fail to stop the onset of infection. Tremendous nutritional demands will be made on the body – especially demand for the B vitamins and vitamin C, and many of the minerals such as zinc, calcium, manganese and chromium; the arteries harden prematurely as tension mounts in the body and the mind, causing havoc to the entire being. And I want to emphasize here that everything that happens to a modern adult under stress also happens to the modern child.

We must realize, of course, that no experience is stressful in itself; stress lies in our own individual response to what is happening to us. We are all biochemically different; our children are unique individuals with special characteristics and special needs, and they all respond differently to different situations. It is important to identify what experiences are stressful to your own child, and then find ways of dealing with them that are acceptable to you both. What had baffled Chris' mother, and had hindered her identifying stress in her son was that his pal up the road always came early to call for him on alternate Thursdays, leading her to think that he looked forward to his trip out of the classroom. Stress to one child might be sheer pleasure to another. Remember, too, that there are anxieties that belong to certain age groups, and that there are differences between the anxieties of adolescent girls and adolescent boys. Furthermore, a child might well be able to cope with one or two stresses – such as end-of-term examinations – but if, at the same time, the child has quarrelled with their best friend, and heard mother or father threaten to walk out on the family – this could well result in an unbearable stress load. In other words, it could result in symptoms ranging from bed-wetting to bad school reports, from sulkiness to stealing. It will certainly result in under-achievement in school, if not complete failure.

CHAPTER 3
IDENTIFYING AND
CONTROLLING STRESS

Let's now work out a plan to identify the specific things which cause your child to feel stress; the factors in your youngster's life that are obstacles to maximum performance in school, the things which disturb and worry them, and those which prevent them from developing into capable, confident and successful students. How can we find out what these obstacles are? Ask them. Ask your youngster whether there are any situations that make them feel terrible, or feel nervous, cause pains in the stomach, or a headache; feel dizzy, feel angry. Is there anything that makes them feel sulky, or unhappy, or unable to breathe properly, or causes the heart to pound or the knees to shake? Is there anything they think about that prevents them from sleeping? is there anything that causes worry or distress? What kind of person gets them upset, or angry, frightens or makes them feel small, inadequate or foolish? Ask what kind of person they find it difficult to talk to and difficult to explain things to.

Ask these questions when you're both in a relaxed frame of mind – mention that you're reading through this book if you like – but do take a casual and relaxed attitude yourself. Try not to pressurise or insist on confidences. How much your child will be prepared to disclose will often depend on their age and your relationship with them. I'll deal later on with this important aspect of communication between parents and children.

While getting this kind of information from your youngsters, make them feel that they're perfectly normal to have this kind of reaction to certain situations. What is most worrying to a teenager, and causes increased stress, is that they think no-one else blushes, or gets butterflies in the stomach, or has to 'swallow' down nerves, or goes completely blank when questioned in a lesson. Give your youngsters examples. Glenys Kinnock has memories of a junior school-teacher who 'rattled off mental arithmetic questions like gunfire'. Her 'whole brain and body would be paralysed with fear' and she could not 'begin to do a calculation'. Many famous and talented people, past and present, have had to conquer nerves, a stutter or stammer, or conceal a disability. Tell your children how you were unable to sleep before a competitive school match, or before examination results. Tell them how you used to have to clear your throat all the time before speaking to a group of people. Give examples of after-effects of stressful experiences. Tell them that older adults don't suffer as many such symptoms as young adults, partly because they've got used to making fools of themselves, and have realized that other people are just as vulnerable as they are. Emphasize that it is very common for youngsters to suffer nervous symptoms; that they're so absorbed in their own anxieties that they don't notice how anxious other people are.

Ask your youngster next what makes them feel great. What causes joy, or pleasure or makes them feel relaxed, comfortable and secure. What makes them look forward?

Take a sheet of paper and write down this information as two lists, this way:

NAME:	
THINGS THAT MAKE ME FEEL AWFUL	THINGS THAT MAKE ME FEEL GREAT

You will probably find that the stressful situations far exceed the pleasant items.

So what do you do with this double list once it's compiled? Take the list of stressful items and divide it into two:

WHAT CAN BE AVOIDED	WHAT CAN'T BE AVOIDED

Now discuss with your child, openly and seriously, what can be avoided and what can't. There will be many things you can sort out quickly and easily together. You will be surprised how easy it is to banish some of the 'bogies'. It is easy to agree on rules for a younger child that an older child's room is out-of-bounds. Other items can be worked out by negotiation and compromise. For example, a child who hates visiting relatives on a Saturday afternoon and prefers to go swimming instead, could be allowed to go to the Pool every other Saturday. It is your responsibility to provide, as far as is possible, an environment that will suit your child, and make their situation as pleasant as possible by avoiding things, such as loud noises, family arguments, or thoughtless remarks, which cause distress.

Your child will understand, depending on age, that there isn't much that can be done about certain stress situations, and that they are bound to experience very stressful situations, at home, and certainly at school. They can't avoid the pressurising of teachers, or losing a friend, nor the difficulties of French pronunciation. Talk about these stresses. Talking about problems is the great giant leap that all parents must take – any other step will be minute in comparison to breaking this ice of communication – but the wonderful thing is, once you've broken that barrier, their problems and anxieties will come flooding out of them.

Then you can go on to the really challenging part; how to teach your child to handle stress. How to master this twentieth century disease and become, in the process, well above average in competence, control, outlook and performance.

Here is my very simple method which has proved to be effective with hundreds of youngsters.

Instant calm

It's a very easy system to manage, whether your child is six or sixteen years old; it's quick; and it brings results.

It comprises three easy stages:

1. Get your child to recognise when they are under stress or likely to be under stress. These are possible signs:

- A nervous twitching of one of the muscles of the face.
- Stuttering.
- Nail-biting or lip-biting
- Tapping the fingers or feet.
- Pounding heart.
- Unexplained headache.
- Upset stomach unrelated to eating.
- Flushing of the face/or pallor.
- Clammy or shaky hands.
- Nausea or disinclination to eat.
- A dry mouth.
- Fear of something happening (apprehension).
- Clearing the throat.
- Constant swallowing.
- Inability to sleep.
- Fast, shallow breathing.
- Forgetfulness.
- Lack of concentration.
- Fidgetiness.
- Dizziness.
- Trembling knees.

2. Teach your child the value of acting a part in order to banish any of these unpleasant symptoms. They must learn

to 'pretend' the way they want to be. Some very interesting
new research at the University of California School of
Medicine claims that we can make ourselves feel confident,
or happy, relaxed or calm, simply by pretending, initially,
that we feel confident when we are not, or relaxed when we
are tense. Tell your child to smile a real smile up to the eyes if
they are feeling down in the dumps. Tell them to square
their shoulders and stand erect if they need to feel confident;
to keep voice and body movements slow and steady when
they feel there's a threat, or a crisis.

3. Teach your child how to breathe deeply. This is the only
way to de-stress in the shortest possible time. When we are
upset or frightened, our breathing is rapid and shallow.
Deep breathing is a very effective technique because it
switches off the stress signal in the brain and persuades the
body that everything is calm and normal. It could, possibly,
too, lower the levels of blood lactate, a substance which is
thought to bring on attacks of anxiety and panic.

Teach your child to breathe in slowly, through the nose, to
the count of five. Hold the breath to the count of five, and
breathe out slowly through the nose to the count of five. Tell
them to imagine that as they breathe out all upsets and
tensions are draining away through the pores of the skin and
disappearing far away into the air.

There is no need for any elaborate technique. A deep, slow
breath is all that is needed. Explain to your child that if they
breathe slowly in and out, when under stress, or when
anticipating stress, the body will automatically decide that
there is nothing to be angry or frightened about, and it will
send a calm and comforting message to the brain.

Please bear in mind that this regime should be made a
daily habit. Take it seriously and practise frequently with
your child. If you do, there will be an extra bonus for you, you
will feel relaxed as well, and more able to tackle the stresses
in your own life. It has been proved that something you do
for twenty consecutive days becomes second nature, so try
this de-stressing regime for twenty days. It is effective with a
young child, an older child, a young adult or an older adult.

That's my three-way plan of stress control. It works. Tell your
child to practise and practise the technique. Emphasise the

benefits of it until the benefits become obvious to your youngster, and until they realise that they can be in complete control of their emotions and their life. The confidence that this gives is wonderful to see, and the benefits are tremendous. They do justice to themselves in every situation; they are calm and confident; learn better and perform well. They meet every challenge with confidence and are happy, motivated and co-operative. This is the road to real success.

Part II
THE PARENT'S ROLE

Chapter 1.
Building up confidence

Chapter 2.
Creating the right environment

Chapter 3.
Dealing with discipline

Chapter 4.
Motivating your child

Chapter 5.
When to start

CHAPTER 1
BUILDING UP
CONFIDENCE

Now that we've put your daughter or your son under a microscope, it's your turn next to be examined. What are you like as a parent? Is it important what kind of parent you are in the overall campaign to get your child to achieve maximum success? It's vitally important! Behind every achieving child there is a motivated parent and when I use the word 'parent', please take it to include anyone who performs the role of bringing up the child in question. How many marks would you score in a parent test? Not that there ever was or ever will be a perfect parent; there is no such phenomenon. No-one is demanding perfection from you, either. If you do give yourself a lesser grade than A, don't be disheartened. It is only in the process of bringing up children that we learn from our mistakes and thereby perfect ourselves, and there are guidelines here on how to modify yourself, improve and change as a parent, so that you will get the very best possible out of your child, in your personal relationship with them, and the very best possible out of their chances of success in school and beyond.

So, here's your test paper. I will sometimes tell a class when I've given them a test: Never mind this time what your marks were, as long as you know where you can improve, and as long as you keep trying to improve. That is the philosophy behind these questions.

1. Do you love your child and completely accept them as a unique human being?

This might appear a strange question to ask. Perhaps you answered the kind of 'Yes' that sounds like 'y-e-e-s', knowing deep down that there is more to it than a plain yes or no. There are very many children – certainly as they go through the adolescent stage – who are very difficult to love, for very many reasons, and there are very many parents who find it difficult to love their children wholeheartedly. These adults could have had undemonstrative or non-loving parents themselves. Anyway, let's assume you were brave enough to answer no. That you don't feel that wonderful emotion towards your child that everyone assumes you feel. Psychologists give this advice:

> Tell yourself over and over that you do love and accept them; that many kids *are* difficult to love, but you're going to love your child and that they are as lovable as any other child that was ever born.

This is a marvellous technique that you can use to achieve what is difficult for you to perform. It's the 'acting' technique again. Tell yourself something often enough and you'll certainly believe it and feel it. Try it for twenty days as you did with the Instant Calm exercise.

2. Now that you are on the way to loving your child, do you show them you love them?

If you've answered no, don't suddenly overwhelm them with frantic hugging and kissing. Make haste very slowly in this area. Try casually holding your youngster's hand or arm when you're asking a serious question. Of course, if you can hug or kiss, and you're used to doing that, there's no problem. Keep hugging and kissing – don't overdo it – when you genuinely feel that it's the appropriate time, for example, when you're saying, 'Oh, never mind, better luck next time' when something hasn't turned out so well for them. A good night kiss is a very good habit to develop and the younger the child, the easier and more natural it is to establish. But, 'never too late' is one of the themes of this book, and I would certainly emphasize this in relation to physical contact. It is just one of the dozens of ways that there are of conveying that you love someone and enjoy their presence. Giving sympathy is a figurative way of 'touching', and showing you care, and youngsters do appreciate sympathy. If your child has fallen out with a friend, then say you're sorry, that you know how it feels and how miserable it is when something like that happens. Try not to take sides; don't judge; never mind who had the greater grievance. Just show how you feel and leave it at that.

Once your youngster knows they are loved, then all kinds of bonuses will occur – they'll be more confident, more secure, and more prepared to show love in return, to you and to others. With some children it will take time – but persevere. Feeling loved and wanted is the most important prop a youngster could have in facing a harsh and demanding world.

3. Have you brought up your child to be confident?

'It's a pity that Julian hasn't got more confidence in himself.'

'Ann lacks confidence in her own ability and this hampers her progress.'

I've read many different versions of these comments hundreds of times on school reports.

For a child to have confidence, they need to be loved and accepted for the unique personality that they are and to be praised for the many admirable qualities they undoubtedly possess. In fact, praise is the most effective confidence-booster of all, for all of us – adults and children alike. You can find some qualities at which you can direct a compliment even in the most difficult child. Give praise when they are on their own and in front of someone else. Give yourself this task to do. Praise your child once in private and once 'in public' for three days running. See the difference it will make. Compliments make for a happier and more secure child who is more confident at tackling every aspect of life, including the most difficult aspect of all – their learning tasks at school.

4. Do you *always*, repeat *always*, take your child very seriously, and listen to their opinions at all times?

You must never, ever, laugh at your child or take them lightly – unless you laugh with them when they tell you a joke. My wife and I learnt this lesson from a most unlikely character. Ron Kempe was a middle-aged bachelor, who would call on us, unexpectedly, from time to time. It was a red-letter day when he called and a topic of serious consideration if he hadn't been around for some time. He never brought the children even the most modest of gifts, but he did one thing that won their hearts completely. He treated them like two wise old women and one wise old man. He would ask them, completely seriously, their opinions about politics, education, and travel. He would always include them in every conversation. When our son was five, and the girls eight and twelve, he discussed with them one evening whether he should go to Egypt or Russia for his half-term October break. Their eyes never left his face and their attention never wavered as he considered each of their opinions in turn. When he returned from Russia and related how he'd been woken in the night, by someone resisting arrest by the KGB, they did not cease to discuss the incident and question him. He answered all their questions as solemnly as if he'd been addressing a contemporary.

Ask your youngster's opinion about personal and private matters; politics; hobbies; travel; education; people. Take their opinions seriously. They become as 'old', as learned, as knowledgeable, as wise, as you treat them. They become confident and secure in the process.

Always be genuine. Tongue in cheek won't do. Our friend Ron Kempe would listen *and* he'd consider the reply. He wouldn't always accept or agree, but he'd consider, very seriously and very sincerely. Use this approach and ask your children questions beyond their years – or what most people think are beyond their years. Probe them about the economy; unemployment; nuclear war; public personalities; drug addiction. Be prepared to listen. Disagree if you wish. But don't think about anything else while you're listening. Listen with completely undivided attention.

5. Can you talk to your child? Can they talk to you? Can you communicate? Can you win their confidence? Can you talk about 'touchy' subjects? Will your child tell you if something is bothering them?

Talking about who might be the next Prime Minister is one thing; disclosing a weakness or a worry is another. The latter requires far more trust by the child, far more loving concern from the parent and far more delicacy in handling the situation. It is a long-term exercise to get your child to confide in you. The earlier it is started, the better, but it is *never* too late.

One of the ways of doing this is to be always on the alert. Try to be aware if there's anything bothering your child – by now you know most of the symptoms of stress. Tell them you realize that something is bothering them, and do they want to talk about it? It's not an easy task to get a youngster to confide worries or admit to a weakness or failure. If they do it once, and you handle the confidence with sympathy and without over-reacting, then the chances are they'll confide in you again. The secret is to be so keen that you keep on trying. That's the type of parent who wins in the end. And a child who can confide in someone has the confidence and self-respect to tackle most of the problems they'll meet, with the obvious bonus that a problem discussed with an under-standing adult is well on the way to being solved.

A youngster can be painfully touchy and non-communi-cative about two things:- a physical oddity or disability, and an inability to perform a task that others of their age-group can manage well. Bring things like this into the open. Our eldest crushed the middle finger of her right hand when she was five, so badly it just escaped amputation. The finger is quite disfigured. From the start, we made a point of talking about the finger – to family and friends and acquaintances, mentioning it naturally 'in passing', even sometimes as a time-guide. 'Oh yes, I remember, it was when you could go swimming again after your finger healed.' When showing photographs, we included some taken in the hospital with her hand on a stand, or at the beach where she'd have a plastic cover over her hand to keep it free from sand. She was never self-conscious about the finger because the whole topic was so much in the open.

Mark, in my wife's English class, had never told anyone – least of all his parents – that he hated being called Dumbo because his ears stuck out. He mentioned it in an essay on 'Things I Dislike'.

So make sure that such matters are brought into the open and are topics of kindly discussion. If your child has protruding ears, buck teeth, a chipped tooth, etc., then you should move heaven and earth to get these minor deformities corrected if the child is bothered about them. If nothing can be done, the youngster, with your help, will accept the situation and adjust.

As for failures and weaknesses, often to do with school work, try and give them an airing as well. At a New Year's Party the parents of a boy in my Physics group began talking to me. Their son was with them and we talked through the son's difficulties for about an hour. I discovered later, from the father, that this episode had formed the basis of a new openness and confidence in their relationship.

Another way, of course, of encouraging your youngster to confide in you, is for you to confide in them – about your own relationships, with relatives and friends, or your own frustrations and inadequacies at work.

CHAPTER 2
CREATING THE RIGHT
ENVIRONMENT

1. Carl, a bright fourteen-year-old, very interested in Science, was in trouble with every member of staff who taught him. A colleague wrote on his report that he couldn't understand why Carl was such a homework dodger. Not only that, he persistently mislaid his exercise and his text books. In anger one day I decided Carl should complete a whole week of sitting in my Laboratory at lunchtimes, after he'd been for his meal, and catch up on missing Physics homework. No problem. Carl was there every day with his bright face and eager smile, bearing me no grudge. On the last day of detention he said to me: 'Can I come here some lunch times from now on, Sir, and do my other homework as well? It's lovely and quiet in your Lab.'

Taken aback, I questioned him and it seemed that, with a brother at home who went to bed very late, and a baby in the household, the home environment, though it seemed a happy one, was too noisy and disorganized for him to settle. So that's where he now does most of his homework, and he keeps all his books on one shelf set aside in the store cupboard.

2. Alison, well-spoken, intelligent and well-behaved, performed very badly when a test or examinations came around. I spoke to her one day about it, but she was a bit loathe to disclose her revision habits, so I left it. I thought I'd have a go another time. I didn't need to. 'You did well in your exams Alison,' I remarked when I signed her next report. 'Yes, Sir, my Gran's come to live up the road, and I go there to revise in the week.' I don't know what had prevented Alison from revising at home, but it's enough to

know that she is able to study at her Gran's.

This is a chapter, mostly about practicalities, that might need adjusting before your child can become a high flier. Is there anything about your household that stops your child from achieving their best work? The kind of environment you have in your home is of paramount importance to your child's success at school, and to their behavioural and intellectual development. It is vitally important that a child of secondary school age has a room of their own where they can study, read, pursue a hobby, think, and have complete privacy. Teachers call this kind of household 'homework conducive', but of course it is conducive to a great number of other things as well, not least being the satisfaction of the basic human instinct to possess your own territory, and the dignity which this allows an adult or a child. Of course, this is not always possible, and where it isn't practical to give a youngster a room of their own, some sacrifices will have to be made by other members of the household. The lounge, for example, could be made into a quiet place, say for three evenings a week, and the television and radio would have to be off for these periods of time. I've known this system to work very well.

Go to great lengths to ensure that a student has a study. We once changed what was meant to be a dining-room into a study, and ate in the kitchen, which was a most successful arrangement. Have two younger ones sharing so that the eldest can have a bedroom cum study of their own. Take out your odds and ends from the box room and line one wall with bookshelves: a study need not be large. See that it is warm, comfortable and has a simple desk to work at. Don't be tempted to knock a wall down to make two rooms into one if you have school-age children. Noise, in the form of all those unnatural noises that people make or create, are very stressful to a student, and there is a lot you can do to block off noise in a household. There *must* be an area where school-children can find peace and quiet to read and think and study.

Incidentally, make sure your youngster knows that you're juggling the house around for their benefit. If they feel that *you* think it's important for them to study, the chances are that *they'll* get the message that it's important to study as well.

I firmly believe in routine, with set times for certain activities. It is best to establish a routine at an early age, and then there's no fuss. All children like routine: it makes them feel secure, that someone cares enough to organize their activities. It is a good idea to establish at an early age that weekdays are for working and weekends for relaxing. Point out to them when they're older that this is what successful professional and business tycoons do.

This might surprise you initially, but in connection with television viewing, I must mention the best buy you could possibly make to ensure peace and industry in your week-day household – a video-recorder. If 'all the kids in my class are watching "Revolt of the Red Robots" on Thursday evening', from 10.15 p.m. to midnight, your thirteen-year-old can always tell their pals:

'I was pushed for time (or tired) last night, but I recorded it for Saturday.'

They won't, then, be considered an oddity, their pride won't be hurt, their status won't be damaged, and the remark could even give rise to some critical opinions as to whether the film was worth retaining or not. An added bonus a recorder gives is that quite young children who want to record a programme will soon find out how to use one properly, and they will learn to store, reject and generally evaluate what they have recorded. In my experience, they become more selective generally about television pro-grammes.

This brings me to bedtime hours and its attendant arguments and problems. A routine in this area, too, works wonders. Too many youngsters are pale, bleary-eyed and yawning in both morning and afternoon lessons, many of them far from wide-awake enough to do justice to their abilities. Older children in Junior School need to be in bed by nine on school evenings, so do the Junior children of Secondary School. Older Secondary School youngsters should be in bed by 10.00 p.m. to 10.30 p.m.

As I mentioned before, it's much easier if routines are established at an early age, at least a couple of years before Secondary School. When you start you need to be brave and persistent. The best plan is to talk about your intentions; lay your ideas on the line and discuss and make a list of the pros and cons of any routine you wish to establish, and give it a trial. Putting your foot down is one way of establishing a routine. Remember those two words NO and YES. It does take courage to use whichever one you need, but they are most productive little words. I meet many parents nowadays who are afraid of being firm – and you can be firm in a kindly fashion – but when they can bring themselves to lay down the rules their household is a different place.

Bribery and corruption is another way of enforcing a routine and I quite like a combination of the two methods! Set times for study, for viewing, for 'going to bed', a set rota for washing up, dusting, hoovering, walking the dog, or mowing the lawn. If these are agreed to who knows what Santa might be persuaded to bring along. Possibly something that would have been in his sack *anyway*.

It's easier in some respects if there are two parents working in harmony on a plan of campaign and providing each other with moral support. On the other hand, if you're bringing up a child on your own, there are still advantages of a different kind. A couple can often disagree about a particular line to take with a youngster. The impact of the one parent, if that parent is caring enough, can be greater. The child depends on one alone and there can be no playing off of one against the other. Take full advantage of whatever 'parent' situation you happen to be in.

So let's have a check list:

1. Is the household reasonably quiet and organized?

2. Does television or anything else – such as ultra-tidiness – 'rule' the household?

3. Does your youngster have their own area where they can follow their own pursuits in private?

4. If you're very short of space, is there a relative who lives within a safe distance who could provide a study for an hour or two on week-day evenings? I've seen this arrangement work wonders with many older students.

And a few things to stress upon your youngster that you mightn't have realized yourself.

1. The rewards of effort and routine are not instantaneous, but every effort, by you and your child, is worth it a million times over.

2. It is a fact that some pupils work very hard at their studies at home. But there's a strange quirk about most youngsters. They'll never admit to studying; never, ever. No, they never study; they were out all evening; no, they couldn't be bothered. And peer pressure is a very powerful force. Point out to your youngster that they shouldn't believe everything their pals tell them.

3. Don't fall for the old time-tested hyperbolical utterances – 'hyperbole' is the literary term for 'fib' and very dramatic and heart-rending they certainly can be.
   Examples of hyperboles:

   (a) 'All my class are allowed to go to "The Nag's Head" any night of the week.'
   (b) 'Everyone in school gets at least £5 pocket money a week.'
   (c) 'No-one at all in my class has to help with the Saturday shopping.'
   (d) 'Everyone's going to Tony's nightclub this Friday.'
   (e) 'Every girl in school is dyeing her hair this Christmas.'

Your youngster may feel they are condemned to being the odd one out but you must maintain your own rules. Tell them that what 'everyone' does is not your concern – but their welfare and well being is.

CHAPTER 3
DEALING WITH DISCIPLINE

'I can't get Wayne to do a thing; he just refuses to do what I ask, whether it's mowing the lawn or going to bed.'

'If I forbid Ian to do anything, he'll be sure to go and do just that.'

'Laura sulks for days if we cross her in any way, or if she can't get what she wants.'

'I think the only thing Wendy enjoys these days is a row.'

What is it in the personality of a parent or a teacher that filters down to a child and persuades them to obey instructions and observe the rules? In other words, how do some people keep discipline and others not? Many a time I've seen two different teachers confronting the same class on the same morning or afternoon. For the one, the members of the class behave and learn and would not dream of stepping out of line. For the other, pandemonium breaks loose.

So what is it about having good discipline that seems so elusive a commodity to a lot of teachers, and a lot of parents? I found that, whether operating as teacher or as parent, you can't go wrong if you keep to these principles.

1. Make it clear that you're on their side and it's their welfare that's important to you.

2. Always be firm and fair, rewarding or praising good behaviour as well as condemning or penalizing unacceptable behaviour.

3. Whatever statement or threat that you make, you must follow it through without fail.

4. Have complete confidence in the validity of what you're doing; with practice, you can persuade yourself, or 'act', into a confident frame of mind and manner.

5. Always ask for and listen to a child's side of the story or argument. Try not to make a hasty decision. If you do make a wrong decision, as you inevitably will from time to time, always admit it and apologize. Never, ever get into a state of non-communication.

Teenagers need the security that comes from knowing you can discipline; that, if need be, you will put your foot down; that a line has to be drawn and that you are in charge of drawing that line. You can discuss and you can compromise, but your youngster must learn that it is you who has the final say. We counsel many parents in school who cannot bring themselves to be firm and say, 'no', or 'enough is enough', or 'you certainly will, or won't'. Their children are sulky and unhappy, because there is no-one in overall control, or are disobedient and confused because too much freedom is too much responsibility, too soon. I have known many parents who were far too lenient and long-suffering. When encouraged to be firmer, they have found almost instantaneous and dramatic improvement in their child's whole demeanour. I had a discussion with a group of fourth formers over a year ago – What would they like more of at home and at school? Discipline!

Supposing your youngster is still persistently disobedient – let's say, about the time they come home from a pal's house in the evenings. In such a case, you'll really have to get down to sorting things out. Are you talking and listening? Are there tensions in the family causing stress? Should you pay the school a visit to see whether there's anything going on that you don't know about? Are you too strict, too unreasonable? Don't be too 'tight' as the kids say, or the child could revolt against all your values. Don't be too rigid, or too easy-going. Don't impose rules and operate changes without giving reasons. Don't apply sanctions without discussing them. But keep firm; dig in your heels. Keep smiling and be optimistic. You – and your child because of you – will win through and succeed.

Be consistent above all else. Don't ignore rudeness one day and become furious about it the next. Don't say they can one week and they can't the next.

The age-old system of reward and punishment is still perfectly feasible and logical. Only you can tell how to reward a child – it depends to a large degree on the hobbies or sport they are interested in – and the task rewarded can be as different as taking in the washing and folding it away every night or helping to look after elderly relatives.

Rewards are the most desirable of course, but don't be afraid to punish. Many parents are afraid of withholding privileges. If your teenager repeatedly comes in a great deal later than expected on evenings out, then it is perfectly reasonable not to allow them out for evenings for a period of time. It'll make the point if you feel confident of your own values and motives. Some parents fear that the child will withhold affection in the face of discipline, and that this will affect their relationship in the future. Children are not made like that. They might appear to do so temporarily, but I can assure you it will be very short-lived. You must never be afraid of short-term unpopularity. Think of the long-term. Out of it all will come respect for you and a new security for your youngster.

There will be many times you'll feel like giving up, that you're getting nowhere – but you are! You'll win eventually, possibly after a great deal of perseverance and many set-backs, and the rewards will make every effort worthwhile.

CHAPTER 4
MOTIVATING YOUR CHILD

Parents often ask what they consider to be a very difficult question.

'How do you motivate a child who is not motivated – who has no wish to learn, who has no ambition, nothing they wish to strive for, and no plans for the future?'

Most certainly these children are increasing in number. They are failing at school through lack of 'drive' rather than inability. Drive is a very popular word with teachers and educators these days because we are worried that there are fewer and fewer youngsters who have real drive, who have the ambition and the motivation to strive and study, win and succeed. What, as a parent, can you do about an unmotivated or apathetic youngster?

Most of my answer to this you will find in the section on the effects of diet on a child's learning power, behaviour and attitudes in general, an area to which I have become very committed. For example, a child who is not getting enough vitamin C can show symptoms of listlessness, apathy and laziness. In a young child, and a young adult – in fact in people from nine to ninety – there should be no such symptom as an inability to get enthusiastic about the future. It must be remembered as well, in connection with this highly important vitamin, that any kind of stress means a dramatic lowering of the body supply of Vitamin C. It is the vitamin which ensures mental well-being in adults and children alike: it is the vitality vitamin, the enthusiasm promoter.

Other vitamins your child will need in order to be alert and energetic are the range of B vitamins. Shortage of these – or any one of these – will soon produce apathy, a lack-lustre look, confusion and often depression. A gloomy outlook can be a sign of a deficiency of one of the B vitamins, especially of niacin and B6, both of which are part of the whole B complex. A deficiency of Folic acid, another part of the B group of vitamins can cause a kind of withdrawal from life, with apathy again as a symptom, and a general slowing of the mental processes of the mind. The consumption of refined and processed foods, together with too high an intake of salt, sugar, fat and additive-ridden junk foods can have the most negative and damaging effect not only on your child's ability to learn and remember, but on their attitudes and personalities as well.

But more – much more – about the effect of what your child eats in the next section. In the meantime, remember that if you are well-motivated, your child has a good chance of being enthusiastic about life in general. If you yourself are looking forward rather than backwards, your child will more than likely get the idea. If you have hobbies and interests, you *will* look forward; if you have something planned for the future, you will be optimistic. Ask your children some very important guessing questions.

1. What do you think you'll be doing two years (or five years, or ten years) from now?

2. Guess what plans I've got for the garden when you kids no longer need a goal post on the lawn.

3. I can't decide what evening class to go to this autumn – what do you think? I'd like to go to Bee-keeping, but I'd like to go to Keep-Fit and Computers as well.

Expose your children to people who are motivated and full of plans and ambitions. Take your youngster to visit Uncle Ted who enthuses continually about the small-holding he'll manage when he's retired from selling cars, or Uncle Joe who, at the age of seventy-seven, is teaching himself Russian in order to read Tolstoy in the original.

Part of the answer, too, to this complex question of motivation, is that you need to do some detective work. In fact, that is what bringing up children is really about – discovering the needs of your special child and finding out what makes them tick. Make a point of finding out what your child has a flair or an aptitude for and then provide all the encouragement you can to pursue a particular interest or hobby. Show interest in every aspect of your child's life and introduce them to as many options as possible – something will appeal to them eventually. Don't, however, force an environment which suits *you* on a child whose needs could well be quite different. A quiet child, for instance, enjoying non-team pursuits, will not want to be organized into a sporting activity involving a lot of noise and physical participation. Be very careful not to force, and wait with patience until it's the right moment to encourage and possibly participate.

There is such a wide variety of options for a child these days – the area of sports activities is an example – that your youngster will surely find something that appeals to them, and most schools have a choice of indoor clubs and outdoor pursuits.

But don't force the issue. Don't panic and don't worry. Provide the environment, stimulation and security, and all of a sudden – BANG – they want to be Prime Minister, and nothing will stop them!!! If they want to be a dress-designer or a fireman, encourage them. If they want to swim or race cars, encourage them. Don't regard their dreams as fantasies and impossibilities. Take them into different work places and help them see work as enjoyable so they will want to get a satisfying and challenging job.

There are a number of 'old-fashioned' truisms that are extremely effective indoctrinations. Remind your child of these from time to time.

1. That school is regarded by most older people as the most pleasant time of their lives.

2. That most pupils who have wasted their time in school regret it and wish they could have that time over again.

3. That a sound education resulting in good qualifications does not automatically guarantee an interesting job, but there is still no doubt that a youngster who is educated and qualified has a head start.

4. That participation in what school has to offer makes a foundation for a worthwhile and satisfying life.

You can train your child to 'look forward' with optimism and excitement, because a feeling that life is exciting and interesting is often a programmed response. It's up to you to do the programming so that your child has ambitions they will go all out to achieve.

CHAPTER 5
WHEN TO START

When our three were born, you were failing as a parent if you didn't have a Reading Scheme and a Maths project ready for the baby the minute they were born! That is a bit of an exaggeration, but there had been a mania, which had crept steadily from the States, for pouncing on a new-born baby and tackling almost at once the task of forming a genius. From this mania sprang the idea that any later than babyhood was too late.

Luckily, we soon realized that all this was quite ridiculous. There is no proof that I can see for going overboard with a young baby in this way with a view to developing superior intellectual ability. Dr Aidan MacFarlane, who is President of the Pre-School Playgroups Association, says that no-one has produced any evidence that this very early stimulation produces baby geniuses who grow up into adult geniuses. In fact, Martin Bax, a well-known neurologist, says that the whole craze of trying to train baby academics 'is a dangerous game and there is thought to be no evidence that it has ever produced a brighter baby'. Martin Richards of the Cambridge Child Care and Development Group claims that people make far too much fuss about teaching a child during babyhood. In fact, a recent study of top students in America showed that it was a good teacher who had the most effect on the performance of ten to fifteen year olds, whether in academic subjects or in sport.

The reason I'm giving you these pieces of research is to stop some of you who might be panicking and thinking that you have missed out because you didn't start when your child was young enough. Let me reassure you: it is never too late.

However, I do believe that if you can start early with a child, in an easy and relaxed manner, making learning a pleasurable game, then your child will have a head start. An excellent guide in this area is Ken Adams' book *Your Child Can Be a Genius and Happy* (Thorsons, 1988) which will certainly set you off on the right path. But to any parent of a baby or toddler, I would certainly stress that you are your child's first and by far their most important teacher. The kind of teacher that only a loving and caring adult can be in a one-to-one relationship, who prepares a child's mind for a happy, receptive attitude to learning during the formative years, when patterns of attitude and behaviour are formed and when the brain is developing at a very rapid pace.

If you claim that you didn't do so well at school, or are not very academic, or don't have any training as a teacher – never mind. This is not what counts. There is no need to wonder or worry whether your results will be good or whether your child will turn out to be intelligent or not. It is well within your capacity to develop in your child the ability to speak and think and reason, and to enjoy finding out, that every child possesses; it is a pleasurable and satisfying task as well.

Talk to your young child sensibly and in complete sentences. From an early age, point out words for objects inside the home and when you're out walking or shopping. If you surround them with words and with talking, they will become naturally fluent and eager to express themselves, in both concrete and abstract language. It is a characteristic of all successful people that they are able to communicate fluently and effectively. Encourage your child to repeat words after you; encourage the formation of sentences; recite rhymes and jingles and read from stories and poems. Praise their efforts and correct them pleasantly. Give them a chance from an early age to talk to the adults that you know and include them in whatever conversation is going on.

Encourage your young child to explain their activities, and all the while, train yourself to listen and always to show a real, genuine interest in everything they do.

This is teaching at its best. Your involvement and interest in their activities and affairs will develop into a bond you can build and then draw upon in later years.

Part III
NUTRITION

Chapter 1.
Identifying difficulties

Chapter 2.
Looking at your child's diet

Chapter 3.
The effects of food on behaviour

Chapter 4.
The necessary nutrients

Chapter 5.
Things to avoid

Chapter 6.
The use of supplements

CHAPTER 1
IDENTIFYING
DIFFICULTIES

There are some things about your son or daughter that your best friend won't tell you; your neighbours or your relatives probably wouldn't tell you either. But a teacher will – teachers are the most insulting people in the world and their stock-in-trade is the scathing remark. These types of comment, be they many, or few, or just one, are extremely upsetting to a conscientious parent.

You might be told that your child is badly behaved in one way or another, possibly that they are over-active, restless, or loud; that they disturb others in class; they snatch or throw things, push or fight; act the class clown; are unable to listen for the required length of time; or incapable of giving an assignment its necessary quota of effort. They might be sulky when reprimanded, denying any accusations and claiming that 'everyone' picks on them. Their work might be below average for the group – and their spelling, writing and numeracy might be generally below the class average.

I can think of at least half a dozen children in every one of my classes who would answer to many of these descriptions and so could many other teachers. They're not extreme cases at all, and hardly stand out as severe behavioural or learning problems as they would have done a few decades ago. We're tending to accept children like this as commonplace. Sadly, these children do not learn and do not succeed.

In any case, if a teacher were to accuse your child of having any of the problems I've just mentioned, you probably would have suspected, before an interview or parents' evening, that they were underachieving. You would probably not have been entirely happy about what was happening in school. You might have been expecting more from your child, without quite knowing what. It's true that parents look at their children through the proverbial rose-coloured glasses, but why shouldn't you? You know instinctively that your child has tremendous talent and amazing potential. So why this vague discontent, this intuitive feeling that something is not quite right?

A mother rang me asking if her son was all right.

'I hate to bother you, and I must sound daft, but is Mark all right?' were her very words. It might sound a ridiculous question but it isn't at all. And no, Mark was not all right.

There were problems, and the mother must have known intuitively that all was not well.

Look at these comments – all taken from the actual, recent reports of children in my own school or my wife's. They are not considered unusual or alarming. Do any of them sound like someone you know?

'Darren is very restless in class and takes a long time to settle.'

'Ann's behaviour is very erratic. In co-operative mood, she contributes and learns, but there are other times when she is moody and unco-operative.'

'Andrea is a bright and intelligent girl, but she is not consolidating learning work. She needs to spend more time on homework, and more time revising.'

'James seems tired in class and tells me he sits up late watching videos.'

'For some reason or other, Jo is not fulfilling the promise he showed in the first and second years.'

'Tim lacks enthusiasm these days, and his work has deteriorated.'

'Vicky has lost confidence this term for some reason, and is too hesitant to trust her own judgement.'

So what's to be done about these vague symptoms? What would you say to your child's teacher in answer to one or more of this type of comment about your youngster?

I've certainly had a variety of replies and suggestions from parents throughout the years, most of them very sensible, very constructive, and displaying great care and concern for the child. Many of them, I must point out, provided a complete solution to the problem.

'Mr Roberts, I know Philip's been impossible this term. I re-married three months ago and Philip's been ten times worse – he's sulky and rude and won't settle to anything. I'm hoping things will get better and my husband's being very supportive.'

'I know that Helen's been watching too much television. Now that you mention that she's yawning a lot in class, I'm going to tackle the problem.'

'I know that Tina's been hob-nobbing with much older girls, and I know this isn't a good sign. She's been very irritable, complains she's bored all the time, and I did have a sneaking feeling that she's been playing truant. I've managed to change my job from evenings to mornings by now, and I'll be able to keep a closer eye on her.'

'I'm going to see that Mark gets up earlier in the mornings, so that he can get better organized with his school books, and get to school on time.'

These problems, and many of their solutions, illustrate what I want you to bear in mind at all times: that it is quite vital for you to treat your child as a very special individual with very special, very demanding needs. They illustrate that it's your care and your belief in your child that will see them through all the bad patches. I've met hundreds of parents who show this fantastic commitment to a youngster, and it rarely fails. I always point out to parents how much more control they have over their child than a teacher has. What an opportunity to mould a future. It isn't so difficult – the process I present to you is foolproof. You'll find the strength if you're committed and convinced.

You know that your daughter or your son will need a secure home environment, with support and love from you; you recognize that many things cause them stress and that they need you to listen and understand. They also need privacy and quiet; stimulation, exercise and relaxation.

But there is another form of 'nourishment' that I want to concentrate on in this chapter – the most obvious

nourishment of all, so obvious that it is often disregarded –
the nourishment provided by food, which, in the opinion of
a rapidly growing number of nutritionists and educators,
provides the foundation for the proper development of all
other facets of your son or daughter's personality and
talents. Other things being equal – namely the factors which
I've been discussing so far – it could be the final key to
unlocking the tremendous potential of body and mind that
too often lies dormant and undeveloped in so many of our
youngsters, despite the many advantages they get these
days. To use another well-worn metaphor that would get me
no A for my English, correct nourishment from food could
well be the last piece of jigsaw needed to form the complete
and unified and effective whole of your child.

It is the belief of a growing body of Bioecological
physicians – physicians who believe that a natural dietary
approach to problems is far more desirable than the use of
drugs or even expert counselling – that the difference
between a child who is marginally nourished and an
optimally nourished child, can sometimes be astounding.
The former would have a diet high in sugar, sugary food and
processed and refined foods, whereas the latter would have
a wholesome, well-balanced and varied diet. I have seen
children whose change of diet has been for the better: their
thinking becomes better organized, the framework of understanding enlarges, and perception is enhanced. The child's
resistance to stress and to infection increases, and they feel
generally stronger, happier and more alert. They take an
increased responsibility for themselves and become more
considerate of others, becoming a more socially effective,
communicative, loving and learning person. To quote from
Allan Cott's *The Orthomolecular Approach to Learning
Disabilities*:

> 'There is rapidly accumulating evidence that a child's
> ability to learn can be improved by... improvement of his
> general nutritional status.'

To stress the point still further, there is such overwhelming
evidence today that a youngster's eating habits are directly
related to behaviour and to mental ability that only an
ostrich with an exceptionally long neck would disregard the
evidence.

We must remember, too, that nourishment occurs in the nine months before a child is born. There is increasing evidence to show that a pregnant woman's nutritional status can be the environmental factor that exerts the most powerful influence on the child for the whole of its life. Even before conception a couple should make certain wherever possible that their diet is nutritionally superior. The mother should guard against anyone – other than a nutritionist – who tries to persuade her to cut down on food to avoid weight-gain, or who suggests drugs such as tranquillizers or diuretics. Two or three children in quick succession is not a good idea either, because the mother needs to regain a high level of nutrients before more demands are made on her body's reserves.

CHAPTER 2
LOOKING AT YOUR
CHILD'S DIET

Do you find it difficult to believe that a change of diet could dramatically alter the life and prospects of your daughter or your son? Or yourself? I suppose it does seem amazing, and yet it isn't really. I've seen it happen, time and time again, this fantastic transformation in a child who has been poorly nourished and whose diet has subsequently been improved. It's such a tragedy that so many people underestimate the power of proper nutrition, and they are often caring people who are well-qualified in methods of psychology, psychiatry, education and counselling.

Our lives revolve to a great extent around food. We in the affluent areas of the world eat four or five times every day of our lives and many people spend a great chunk of their waking hours planning and preparing meals. Right from the beginning of time, food has played a prominent and crucial part in our lives, and even from very ancient times people believed that fresh food prevented and cured ailments and diseases. Feasts were held to celebrate victory in battle; banquets were held at auspicious times of the year, and today people celebrate at the slightest excuse with a 'slap-up' meal, for birthdays, weddings, anniversaries and special events such as Christmas.

So what about the food our children are eating today? Is there really cause for concern? Is it damaging our physical health and levels of energy? Is it causing severe emotional, physical and learning problems?

There has been a lot of publicity given during these last few years to the diet of our children, certainly from the point of view of the effect on their physical health.

From Woman – *8 March 1986.*
'Malnutrition is not only something that affects people in Third World countries. In relatively prosperous Britain today, thousands of children are growing up on vitamin-less diet, existing mainly on crisps and cola.'

From Today – *4 April 1986.*
'The Government has denied suppressing a report which shows that Britain's children may be eating their way to an early grave. A survey of more than 3000 children aged 10 to 15, revealed they are eating too much fat and sugar which could lead to heart disease and cancer. It also showed that their diet is so unbalanced they depend on chips, cakes and biscuits for vital nutrients.'

From Healthy Living – *February 1986.*
'The part food plays in schools these days is often little short of scandalous. Many school meals are now cafeteria style to save money. Pupils are no longer presented with a carefully balanced meal on a plate, designed to provide much of what is required by a growing child. Instead, in the interests of short-term economy, children are being encouraged to ruin their long term health. Reports make it clear that in some the rot has already set in. Many teenagers carry the beginnings of fatty deposits in their arteries which will predispose them to early coronaries.'

The problem is, of course, that the effects of an inadequate diet is not always obvious, except in extreme cases. Because a child does not display symptoms of scurvy, it doesn't mean that their intake of Vitamin C is adequate. The difficulty is that there is no firm, clear-cut boundary separating A Good Diet and A Bad Diet. The effects of a bad diet are not at all easy to detect and could be caused by other factors, the symptoms are so subtle and so vague. A child won't collapse in a coma, but might display some of the many symptoms of a low-nutrient diet: lack of motivation; lack of perseverance; lack of concentration; lack of stamina; lethargy; irritability; mild depression; anxiety; poor memory; school phobia; learning difficulties. There is no doubt whatsoever that an ever-increasing number of infants, juniors, pre-teens and teens are suffering from physical, behavioural and learning disorders. All these unexplained symptoms are baffling to parents and teachers, and baffling even to the youngsters themselves.

These symptoms, of course, although vague, are just what could spell the difference between success and failure, and because the education and the development of ability in youngsters is such a subtle and sensitive area, once a child sets even a foot on the slippery slope to under-achievement, it is very difficult to get back on an even keel. It's no use providing *most* of the ideal conditions for the success of your daughter or son: getting nine out of ten is no use in this area. The tenth factor might be *THE ONE* which will enable all the others to work. *ALL* possibilities that might benefit your child must be explored; *EVERYTHING* must fit into place. The main theme of this book is 'Balance'; it is a consideration of *all* the possible factors which could affect the development of youngsters, and this is something which has not been done before, even by the most caring and persevering of educators. Bringing up children into the teenage years is thrilling and exciting, and a great adventure for parents, but you need all the resources that science and imagination have devised.

Also, it's so easy to blame the child and label them as idle, lazy, disruptive, or lacking in motivation without exploring all the possible reasons why their behaviour and learning performance are not acceptable and not conducive to development and success.

I suppose it is difficult – if you have not met these ideas before – to accept the proposition that something as obvious and common-place as the food youngsters consume has, in many cases, *everything* to do with many unexplained symptoms. Would you question your child's diet if his performance at school were poor, especially if you'd explored other possibilities? Many enlightened parents are starting to do just this. One mother wrote to me last year and this is part of her letter:

'My son's behaviour deteriorated after we sent him to boarding school in April last year ... we eventually came to the conclusion it might be because of the heavy load of additives he was consuming with all sausages, fish fingers, chips and bright yellow smoked fish, etc., he was being given.'

Indeed, his additive-ridden diet did turn out to be the reason for the deterioration in behaviour in her son; she herself did not use convenience foods at home, read labels conscientiously and had already changed over to wholemeal flour and had cut down on sugar. She says she had a totally different child at the end of about two weeks of his Easter holidays.

Let me explain what has happened. Over the last couple of decades the pace of life has become more and more hectic and inevitably, there has been less time to think about and prepare meals. As a result, we've seen a huge explosion in the 'convenience' food market, and this new, lucrative market has prompted intense competition between food manufacturers: it is vital for food to look attractive, to have a pleasant taste, and to have as long a shelf-life as possible. The outcome is that most of the nutrients have been removed from foods, to be replaced by bright colours, artificial flavours, preservatives, sugar, fat and salt. In some ways, there has been an improvement. It is quite true that there is greater distribution of food to all members of society, and the standards of hygiene have greatly improved. But the food industry is there to make profits, and no-one would make much profit from a natural potato. Give it fat, salt and additives and the lowly potato, cheap to buy, becomes an expensive packet of crisps. Advertising plays an important part in giving us information about food, but it can be misleading. If you are trying to cut down on saturated fats then you may be tempted by advertisements for a low fat spread which contains half the fat of butter or margarine. What they don't disclose are the acidity regulators, emulsifiers, preservative, flavouring and colouring that are also in it. Adverts for many kinds of yogurt are designed to suggest that it is a very healthy food, but no mention is made that there can be eighteen grams of sugar in one small carton of fruit yogurt. Yes, there is fibre in baked beans, and often no colouring, but there are ten grams of sugar in half a medium tin. We're encouraged to flavour our food with tomato ketchup – no one tells us it's loaded with sugar and salt. In fact, one could think of many foods that are presented as being healthy, but the contents are not so healthy when you read the labels.

I think most people these days would agree that the

connection between good health and the food we and our children eat, is quite clearly proved. This doesn't mean that food is entirely responsible for health or lack of health, but it is certainly a most important factor. The greatest cause of ill-health nowadays must surely be our intake of refined foods from which all goodness has been removed to make it look more attractive – refined fat, refined sugar, refined flour. Anyone wishing to feel on top form must change white flour for wholemeal, refined sugar for a little honey only, and refined fat for polyunsaturated oils, the best of which are sunflower, safflower or olive oil. Also, salt needs to be very sparingly used, or a product such as Biosalt or Rutin used instead of ordinary salt. Enough fresh fruit, dried fruit, and fresh vegetables need to be eaten; natural uncoloured cheeses and low fat yogurt; fresh and canned fish; free range eggs and poultry. Carbonated, sweetened and stimulant drinks – coffee, tea, coke, cocoa and drinking chocolate – should be avoided.

Don't be put off by the term 'whole food'. All it means is foods that are as near their natural state as possible, without anything added or anything taken away. In this state they are more likely to contain the nutrients our bodies need. Take our daily loaf for example. When whole flour is refined to make white flour the B vitamins and many minerals are lost, and so is the wheat bran, the fibre which is so important for digestion and elimination. Fibre is the filler in plant foods that stops us from over-eating.

The colourings and flavourings in our foods are put there to make whatever we're eating more alluring and attractive, but many common food additives are highly suspect and are thought to contribute to all kinds of health problems, allergies and cancer included.

As a nutritionist, I must point out as well that the soil in which food is grown is the basis of good nutrition and good health. Most farmers add chemical fertilizers to the soil and spray crops with chemicals. The food group therefore contains traces of these chemicals which are proven to be harmful. Wherever possible, therefore, try to eat organically grown produce which is free of any of these pollutants.

I'm certain that you are prepared to believe that physically all children, and all adults of course, would benefit from a healthier, more natural, more vital diet. I'm certain, too, that, when you're convinced of this, you will make attempts – not forcefully, but gently and with consideration, over a period of time – to wean your child off junk foods and on to a diet that will keep them in the kind of health that is so necessary a foundation for any success. Don't give up if your child doesn't respond. Don't fret and fume and forbid. It took my wife and I eight years to get our son onto a healthy diet, and it would take another volume to relate the difference it made, not just academically, but to his whole personality.

CHAPTER 3
THE EFFECTS OF FOOD
ON BEHAVIOUR

It's still a very odd idea to many people that what we eat, and what a child eats, affects mental processes, attitudes and behaviour. And yet these very people will comment that delinquency is growing amongst young people and that they have no idea why youngsters are so difficult to manage. As long ago as 1968 *The Times* reported that juvenile crime was increasing in almost every European country, and that the biggest increase was in the most developed industrial nations. Some of the offences mentioned were vandalism, shoplifting, truancy from school, burglary, and violence against people. Sociologists used to blame such factors as poverty, lack of education, or the breaking up of homes and communities for such tendencies among youngsters, but the fact is that many of these suggested reasons – I'm not saying all – have been removed. But, behavioural problems are on the increase.

Obviously there are many factors to consider as explanations for deteriorating behaviour in our youngsters. But there is rapidly accumulating evidence from a number of enlightened doctors, paediatricians, scientists and perceptive observers, that high-quality nutrition can immeasurably improve behaviour and also the ability to learn. A very large and growing number of parents have realized that there is overwhelming evidence for believing that the food their children eat affects both the way they behave and their academic performance in school. These parents are realizing that their offspring will develop well and perform well in school if they are given the kind of nutrients which will keep the body and the brain optimally nourished. These parents are becoming more and more convinced that there is something wrong with the methods and organization of the food industry, and something seriously wrong with most hospital meals, school meals and even meals they provide at home. Many are searching for a much better nutritional regime for their children. They are realizing that the junk food of today is rubbish, nutritionally, and that a child will not develop their full physical and mental potential on poor quality nutrition.

But the concept that food affects the brain is still, quite understandably, not easy for everyone to believe, mainly because the processes of learning are so very complex; when a child is learning something, the intricate biological, chemical, and electrical processes which occur in the brain are still not fully understood even nowadays. Human behaviour, as well, is highly complicated and depends on a correct balance in all kinds of areas such as relationships and environment.

Alexander Schauss is an American who used to be a real disbeliever about the benefits of good nutrition. He started his working life as a probation officer, his task being to inspect homes for delinquent youngsters to see that these children were cared for properly. On one occasion, he arrived at a particular children's home and was told that the children were on a diet of completely natural food, and were given homegrown vegetables, free of additives, wholemeal bread and whole cereals. They were not given tea, coffee or fizzy drinks, nor were they given foods with a lot of sugar in. This was a most unusual dietary regime for the time. The result of it, Schauss discovered to his great amazement, was a transformation in the behavioural and learning patterns of these juveniles who had been considered some of the worst cases of child offenders in the USA.

Schauss discovered that even in homes where the attitude towards these youngsters was very caring and conscientious, the results were nowhere near as impressive as this one particular 'whole food' home. To cut a long story of research and experimentation short:- since that time in the mid-seventies, Alexander Schauss has become a world authority on the effect of nutrition upon the processes of the brain, especially as regards behaviour and learning. He has tested hundreds of youngsters with the 'junk-free' diet, and has found that the young criminals who had committed the worst offences were the ones who showed the most dramatic improvement. Teachers and parents inundated him with pleas for more information, and the whole of America became interested when he appeared on television to expound his new ideas. His book *Diet, Crime and Delinquency* has become a classic in the world of nutrition.

An individual opponent of Schauss was Stephen Schoenthaler, an expert in criminology. He claimed that Schauss was talking nonsense. But he had the good sense to start experimenting himself. He did so, initially, with 68 delinquent children. He threw out the junk food they habitually ate and introduced into their diet natural, nutrient-rich foods. He found the results too dramatic to ignore. He extended the experiment to 276 children, dividing them into two groups, one group eating junk foods and the other group eating a much more nutritious diet. The results he got were amazing, and in another trial involving 17,000 juvenile offenders, Schoenthaler got the same phenomenal behaviour improvement as well.

Very impressive results have been recorded in New York, where not only did children's behaviour improve on being fed a more natural and nutritious diet, but their progress and performance at school showed remarkable improvement. Schools in New York used to be eleven points below the national average in academic performance, but in the four years when school meals included wholemeal dishes, salads, fresh vegetables and fruit, meat and fish, and excluded refined foods, and those containing artificial flavouring and colouring, these schools rose five points above the national average in academic performance.

Another scientist in America who believed that the nerves and the brain cells were affected by diet, just as the cells of the body are affected, was Ruth Harrell, Ph.D. She discovered that something in the B complex group of vitamins, B1 in particular, made the learning process easier and faster. At an Orphans' Home in Virginia she conducted an experiment involving a hundred youngsters in the pre-teen and teenage years. They were divided into two groups, as alike as possible in age, health, intelligence, background and so on. Group A took a B vitamin tablet once a day; Group B took an identical tablet with no vitamin included in its formula – a 'placebo' as it is called. None of the teachers in this home, nor Dr Harrell herself, knew which group took the vitamin and which took the placebo. The only person who knew was a great distance away, so that no personal involvement would affect the results of learning tests which were given regularly to the two groups. It was discovered that the group taking the B vitamins had made greater gains in all areas of learning than the group who had not received vitamins.

To come nearer home, Dr John Dobbing of the Department of Child Health at Manchester University, conducted tests on young children some years ago. These children were not delinquent, but Dr Dobbing found that in these children a poor diet of vitamin and mineral deficient snacks had resulted in various learning impediments, such as inability to remember or poor concentration and study habits, and their confidence and morale were low. An improvement in diet resulted in a much greater ability to cope with learning situations.

By this era of the late eighties, it is the firm conviction of Bioecological physicians – physicians who believe that a nutritional approach is more effective than any other in the promotion of mental and physical health – that a child who is not receiving optimum nutrition is at a serious disadvantage and cannot possibly perform optimally at school. A youngster receiving a range of nutrients in their diet is well-equipped to tackle the hefty physical and learning demands made on them.

CHAPTER 4
THE NECESSARY NUTRIENTS

So that you're completely convinced about the inestimable value of a diet high in nutrients, I will tell you what it is in foods that get the body and the mind functioning at their best. For very detailed accounts of what happens to food in the body and the brain, I would recommend books such as: *A Guide to the Vitamins: Their Role in Health and Disease* by John Marks (MTP Press, 1979), or *Brain Food* by Dr Brian and Roberta Morgan (Pan, 1987), but I will try only to present you with what is relevant and interesting in this particular context of ensuring your child's success at school.

To begin with, nutrients are the substances in food which are crucial for life, which the human being cannot manufacture in their own body, and which has to be obtained from food to function optimally.

They are: 1. Amino acids (protein)
2. Carbohydrates
3. Essential fatty acids (Fats)
4. Vitamins
5. Minerals

Although your child is unique, with special needs of his or her own, there is, nevertheless, a minimum need by the body for all these nutrients. Different children, for various reasons, might need more of one or the other, but there is a minimum which every child, and every adult, needs. These must be provided not only in adequate amounts, but in the correct proportion, and every single one must be available. Each nutrient performs a special job in the body and the brain, either on its own or in combination with other nutrients. Different nutrients are found in different foods, with some foods containing several different nutrients at once. In fact, feeding children optimally is all about balance.

Let me explain how you can get all these nutrients for your child, and what they will do.

1. Protein is an extremely complicated combination of amino acids, and it is the substance from which the body makes and renews the actual body structure. Protein is found in lean meat, fish, low fat cheeses, peas, beans, nuts and eggs. Avoid salted nuts and dry roasted nuts. Your child needs protein in order to grow properly and in order to manufacture and repair the cells of the body and the brain. The process of learning and memorizing involves changes in the nerve cells of the brain, and for these changes to take place, sufficient protein is vital. The need for protein is increased at times of rapid growth, such as the teenage years, and during periods of stress such as intense learning and the sitting of examinations. As, of course, is the need for all the nutrients.

2. Whereas the body 'house' is built mostly of protein it needs to be heated by carbohydrates. They are the energy foods, and should come from complex carbohydrates such as wholemeal bread, brown rice, wholemeal pasta, and jacket potatoes. Sugar is a pure carbohydrate, but most people know by now that it is a very poor carbohydrate and one that causes a lot of problems when taken to excess. I'm talking of course about the white sugar you buy in packets at the supermarket, not the natural sugar in fruit and vegetables. We need the latter kind of sugar, but the refined pure white sugar is a nutritional disaster. The body cannot deal with it in the large amounts contained in the modern refined diet. Yes, it does break down into glucose to provide energy, but the body tries to use it too quickly and then the trouble starts – the sort of trouble that can lead not only to obesity but to tooth decay, diabetes, hyperactivity, hypo-glycaemia and heart disease. It is an anti-nutrient as well because it uses valuable vitamins and minerals to convert the sugar into energy which the body needs.

So the more sugar that's eaten, the more is the vitamin and mineral requirement, and these will be 'stolen' from their more important tasks of feeding the body and the brain. You should rigorously avoid giving your child refined white sugar in any form. This can be difficult as many foods contain sugar – from yogurt to baked beans, not to mention cakes, bisuits, ice-cream and soft drinks. Most breakfast cereals aimed at the 'children's market' contain refined sugar. Raw sugar, and unrefined sugar is nearly as bad, but these are good ways of cutting down the white, as they are so much stronger in taste.

In Britain, each person consumes a horrific amount of sugar, on average – about 100 lb a year, and in fact many children eat far in excess of this figure. You must explain to your child that sugar is very bad for them, and try to avoid buying sweets and chocolates as a treat. There are many other forms of treats and rewards, from nuts and fruit to hugs and privileges. But don't try to abolish sweets overnight. You might have to be content with just cutting down for a while, or having only one day a week as a 'sweet' day. You could try allowing only a certain amount of pocket money per week for sweets.

3. Just as with carbohydrates, some fat is necessary to insulate the body but an excessive amount will soon turn to unwanted body fat and its attendant problems. What we call unsaturated, or polyunsaturated, fats are better than the saturated fats of meat, butter, cream and the white, solid shortenings in which the important fatty acids have been destroyed. The polyunsaturates are mostly found in corn oil, soya oil, sunflower oil and safflower oil, and in the polyunsaturated margarines.

There is a lot of controversy about fats and we are constantly told to cut down. This is good advice as most people eat far too much of the wrong fats, the saturated ones. This is the kind associated with the build up of cholesterol in the arteries, and resultant heart trouble. However, there are certain elements found only in unsaturated fats which are crucial for the well-being of our body and brain. The brain needs the essential fatty acids which manufacture EPA (eicosapentanoeic acid) and DHA (docosahexaenoic acid) as they have very important roles to play in the body's metabolism. They are available only from oily fish such as mackerel or sardines and are an important part of the diet. Cod liver oil is also a valuable supplement to the diet of any child or any adult.

It is important to know that frying foods in oil that is

heated to a high temperature is harmful. If fat or oil is heated to smoking point it becomes toxic and changes the structure of fatty acid, and the balance of nutrients in the oil is changed. Grilling, boiling or baking food is far healthier.

4. The vitamins are next, the minute but powerful substances in natural foods which are the 'spark plugs' of the body. Proteins, carbohydrates and fats can do their work only when there are enough vitamins. So, to maintain health and well-being of body and mind, we must obtain adequate amounts. In the days when vitamins were discovered, and when no-one knew their chemical structure, they were given a letter of the alphabet to distinguish one from the other. Some have been given names by now.

We start with Vitamin A which is found in milk, dairy foods, oily fish and above all in cod and halibut liver oils, the best source of A and D. If dairy foods are the main source of Vitamin A in your diet, then there is the danger that too much saturated fat is being taken at the same time. In this case eating oily fish would be a better idea.

It has been proved that lack of Vitamin A in young children causes brain damage and lack of both protein and Vitamin A can cause severe mental retardation. 'A' is also the eyesight vitamin, and the anti-infection vitamin. For the obvious reason of ensuring good attendance at school, it is important to guard your child against infection. Vitamin D is vital for children because it is needed to help the body use calcium to promote normal bone growth. The B group of vitamins are all closely related, each helping the function of the others.
They are: B1 (thiamine)
          B2 (riboflavin)
          B3 (niacin or nicotinic acid)
          B6 (pyridoxine)
          B12
          Folic acid
          Pantothenic acid
          Biotin
Some nutritionists include choline and inositol as B vitamins, but they are not strictly vitamins because the body can manufacture them. P.A.B.A. and Pangamic Acid are not strictly vitamins either but are usually included in this group. The B vitamins are found in wholemeal bread and

cereals; eggs and fish; liver and green vegetables. They are removed during processing from white flour and refined cereals.

The B vitamins are so versatile, so beneficial to physical and mental health that an adequate supply is absolutely vital for the success of your child because they are essential to all brain functions. Here are a few facts about their benefits and functions.

(a) B1, B2, B6 and B12, with niacin and pantothenic acid, are vitally necessary in building brain cells, and in converting glucose into energy to fuel the brain.

(b) B1 is known as the 'morale' vitamin. Children who eat too many refined and sugary foods seriously lack B1, and can become depressed, lethargic and anti-social. They may develop a craving for all kinds of stimulants. Deficiency can lead to the memory and the ability to concentrate being affected; lack of initiative and irritability can occur. Digestive upsets may be caused by a lack of B1 in the diet.

(c) B2, riboflavin, has the effect of colouring the urine yellow, but this is harmless. A child who has insufficient B2 could have sleeping difficulties, learning problems, and tired or blood-shot eyes.

(d) A deficiency of niacin, B3, can cause moodiness, emotional instability, and poor memory. A Canadian psychiatrist, Dr Hoffer, claims that children who need more than average amounts of B3, and are deficient, display 'overactivity, perceptual changes, difficulty in reading and learning, and changes in personality'. Among teenagers, this demand for B3 can manifest itself in moodiness, anti-social behaviour, and depression.

(e) B6, Pyridoxine, is an anti-depression and anti-allergy vitamin. It is also used in the treatment of pre-menstrual tension.

(f) A deficiency of B12 can cause moodiness, lethargy and poor memory. Anaemia is a symptom of advanced B12 deficiency. It is necessary for a healthy nervous system and in assisting to flush chemical pollutants out of the body.

(g) Pantothenic Acid has an important role in the life of a

student, because it combats fatigue, nervousness, stress and insomnia.

(h) The name Folic Acid is taken from 'foliage' meaning green leaves, as it is found in green, leafy vegetables. It works closely with B12 to ensure the health of the central nervous system. A shortage causes poor memory and irritability, and slows down the intellectual processes of the mind. Again anaemia is a sign of advanced folic acid deficiency.

(i) Biotin is necessary for healthy skin, hair, and nerves; deficiency can cause fatigue, depression and lethargy.

Vitamin C has received a great deal of publicity, and there is no doubt that it is an extremely versatile vitamin. It is needed by every cell in the body and a deficiency will make your child more vulnerable to infection and slower to heal. It helps to absorb iron and is involved in the production of the hormones needed to cope with stress. Any kind of stress, fever or infection, creates a high demand for vitamin C, but, because the body cannot store it, supply is needed on a daily basis. The main source of vitamin C is fresh fruit, particularly citrus, and vegetables. Because C has such a varied role in body functions, a mild shortage cannot easily be identified, but among the first signs of deficiency are bleeding gums and the skin bruising more easily than usual. More advanced deficiency may lead to depression, listlessness, fatigue, disinclination for activity and sallowness or roughness of the skin.

Vitamin E has received its share of publicity as well, probably because of the claim made for it that it is the youth and virility vitamin! It is found in seeds and nuts; cold-pressed oils such as soya or corn oil; wheat germ, rice, cabbage, broccoli and spinach.

Vitamin E helps the body use oxygen properly. It also improves the passage of oxygen to the tissues of the brain, and is important for muscle control and development in babies and older children.

Closely linked to vitamins are the minerals and, of course, I mean the beneficial minerals rather than the harmful ones that I shall mention later. There is evidence now that minerals in the diet are more important than vitamins, and that a deficiency is even more likely because of soil depletion and the refining of foods.

For the purpose of ensuring success at school, the most important of all the minerals is Calcium. It is known to be necessary for healthy bones and teeth, but not so widely known that sufficient calcium is necessary for mental well-being. Deficiency of calcium can cause irritability, depression, poor memory and sleep disorders. Dairy products contain the best calcium, and it is also found in peas, beans, potatoes, cauliflower, molasses and dried figs.

For the body to utilise and absorb calcium properly the mineral magnesium is needed. The amount taken is usually half magnesium to calcium. Magnesium is found in dark green leafy vegetables, soya products and many nuts and grains. These two minerals have a tranquillizing effect on the nervous system, helping you to sleep better at night and be more relaxed during the day. Dolomite tablets are excellent sources of calcium and magnesium. The best drink to give your child to ensure a good night's sleep before an examination is hot milk into which is stirred a teaspoon of honey and a teaspoon of molasses. With this, let them crunch two or three Dolomite tablets.

Potassium is another important mineral, a deficiency of which can cause fatigue, poor appetite and mental listlessness. Grains, fruit and vegetables contain good supplies of potassium. Bananas, dried fruit and molasses are also particularly rich sources.

It is important to note that in a healthy diet, there is always more potassium than sodium, yet, in our salt-ridden Western diet, we consume several times more sodium than potassium.

Trace minerals are very important indeed in their effect on the body and the mind. Zinc is one of these and deficiency of it is widespread. Meat, eggs, milk, mushrooms, onions, wholegrain bread, wholegrain cereals, and seafood are the best sources. Processed and refined foods are rather low in zinc as much is lost in their manufacture. It is very important for the brain and for the learning processes, and it is utilised best when taken with B6. Deficiency can cause mental apathy, irritability, poor memory and tiredness. It is claimed that a deficiency can contribute to anorexia nervosa. Acne, splitting hair, and brittle nails, retarded growth and growing pains can be caused by lack of zinc. A sign of zinc deficiency is flecks of white on the nails.

Generally better known than zinc is iron, another very important mineral. It is widely known that iron deficiency can cause anaemia, particularly in young girls and women. However, lack of some of the B vitamins can cause anaemia as well.

It is extremely important for a school child to obtain sufficient iron because it aids growth, prevents fatigue and helps promote resistance to disease. It is also important in helping the body to metabolise the B vitamins. If your child is pale, has brittle or flat fingernails with longitudinal ridges on them, they could be suffering from iron-deficiency anaemia. Encourage your youngster to eat liver and the organ meats, green vegetables, wholegrains, dried fruit and molasses. The iron in meat is better absorbed by the body than iron in grains.

There is one last mineral that I want to bring to your notice – selenium. It has risen to fame lately because there has been evidence that an adequate amount can help the body to resist cancer, and that it promotes longevity. For our purposes at the moment, it is enough to know that selenium increases the efficiency of vitamin E as an anti-oxidant and that it protects against harmful minerals such as lead and cadmium.

CHAPTER 5
THINGS TO AVOID

One of the problems we have these days that primitive man did not have, is that there are materials in the air, the water and the soil that are very harmful to our bodies and our brains. Many of these substances are more harmful to children than to adults, because the tissues of the young absorb them more readily. There's nothing we can do to get rid of these pollutants – that's twentieth century industrial and technological progress for you – but there is a great deal that you as a parent can do to counteract their toxic effects on your youngster's body and brain.

One of the worst offenders is lead and it is the one that harms children most. It can produce changes in the chemistry of the brain which can lead to hyperactivity, aggression and behavioural and learning problems. So, if your child is over-active or is not learning as they should at school, and you have ruled out other causative factors, then start suspecting lead as the culprit, especially if you live near a road which takes heavy traffic, if there are smokers in the house, if you live in an older property which has lead plumbing, or if you use a lot of canned foodstuffs. In fact, lead is everywhere in the environment. People have known for centuries that there is such a thing as lead poisoning, and that it can be fatal, but it must be remembered that there can be levels of lead, in a child's body especially, which are not fatal but which, nevertheless, cause some very serious dysfunctions. There have been numerous studies and experiments by doctors and scientists which have shown a greater amount of lead than normal in the blood of slow learners, children with low intelligence, and retarded children. The first impressive study about the toxicity of lead was conducted by a professor of child psychiatry, Herbert Needleman, who examined a group of 2,146 young children from schools in Birmingham, in the United States. Needleman determined the levels of lead in individual children by examining the amount of lead in their discarded milk teeth. The results showed a definite link between high lead and poor learning and behaviour. Two psychologists at the University of London conducted the same kind of study, using blood tests this time, and the results showed even more dramatically than Professor Needleman's that there was a correlation between high levels of lead and intelligence and behaviour.

It would be facile of me to tell you to move out of an inner city area or town or away from a major road if you have young children, but if you are thinking of moving house, I would certainly advise you to keep as far from traffic fumes as possible. At least until legislation against leaded petrol is in operation.

The good news is that you can protect your child against the ill-effects of lead with a diet that has sufficient vitamins and minerals. Vitamin C is proven to be an excellent detoxifier, and if the brain is provided with enough iron and zinc it will not absorb lead in anywhere near the degree it would if these beneficial minerals were lacking. Calcium is very important as well in the prevention of lead absorption. But a word of warning. If you give your child Dolomite, as a calcium and magnesium supplement, make certain it is lead-free. Remember, too, that a protein-rich diet is protective because of a variety of beneficial minerals in protein. Vitamin E, whose effectiveness is enhanced by selenium, is a protector as well.

Aluminium is another toxic metal, found everywhere in the environment, which can affect the liver and the kidneys, and also the central nervous system. Again, a diet rich in protective vitamins and minerals is a good safeguard, but it is always wise to avoid cooking equipment made of aluminium. Antacids, baking powder and many deodorants contain aluminium. Avoid them if you can and look for safer, natural alternatives.

The mineral mercury has been associated with brain damage, headaches, depression, insomnia, loss of memory, and hearing and speech difficulties. Large fish, tuna especially, can be contaminated with mercury dumped in rivers and lakes. There is mercury in some cosmetics and in amalgam dental fillings. Vitamin C and vitamin E help to flush mercury from the body, as they do all toxic materials.

Millions of tons of dangerous pollutants are continually released into the air and water, in the form of detergents, household sprays, insecticides, pesticides, fluoride, and various radioactive wastes such as Strontium 90. Try to cut down on chemical toiletries, aerosol cans and scented cosmetics and soaps. If you are a keen gardener, don't spray with chemicals. There have been reports of children whose behaviour has dramatically changed for the better when aerosol sprays and chemical cleaning fluids have been removed from the home. Chlorine in swimming pools can cause symptoms ranging from red, itchy eyes to aching joints and irritability. Many scientific authorities are opposed to adding fluoride to drinking water because it is claimed that there is a connection with Strontium 90, which combines with fluoride to form a compound which becomes deposited in the bones. Fluoride in the body slows down the flushing out of Strontium 90.

A much better idea than fluoridating water would be to concentrate on good dental habits, and encourage the eating of a nutrient-rich diet. If you are really serious about the well-being of your children and yourself, drink bottled mineral water, or fix a filter to your water supply.

Fluoride-free toothpastes for children are a good idea and you could try one of the natural plant-gel ones which are also sugar-free.

There is another area to investigate if your child is hyperactive, is forgetful, anxious, finds difficulty concentrating, is tired for no reason, has migraine headaches, rashes, asthma, bronchitis or exzema. This area is food allergy, an unpleasant reaction to a particular item of food. It is only recently that we have come to understand that the mind as well as the body can react adversely to food and cause behavioural and learning problems as well as undesirable physical reactions. These reactions come and go in a way that is very difficult to diagnose. Very often, though, a symptom of food allergy is a kind of tiredness which persists even after periods of rest.

The foods that most commonly cause allergic reactions belong to the following groups.

1. Wheat, and any product containing it such as bread, cakes, biscuits. Wheat is the most common cause of allergy.
2. Eggs.
3. Milk.
4. Additives in food, such as tartrazine (E102); sunset yellow (E110), or monosodium glutamate, and various other emulsifiers, stabilizers, preservatives and colours. The book *The New E for Additives*, by Maurice Hanssen (Thorsons, 1987), contains everything you need to know about additives in foodstuffs and their effects on sensitive people.
5. Chocolate, tea, coffee.
6. Shell fish.
7. Strawberries and citrus fruits.
8. Cola drinks and foods and drinks containing citric acid.
9. Sugar.
10. Drugs.

Whenever anything enters the body, a message is sent to the brain signalling whether it is 'acceptable' or is a 'foreign' substance. If it is seen as 'foreign' that is when an allergic reaction can occur. Normally, the immune system, a very complex mechanism on which the body depends, processes all foreign substances entering the body and sends its force of white blood cells to attack them once they're there. But if the digestive system and the immune system are not working properly, these irritants or allergens as they're called, will get into the blood via the skin, or the mucous membranes of the nose, lungs or intestinal tract and cause irritation or inflammation. To avoid or minimise any allergic reactions the diet should contain a high protein intake and a good supply of vitamins. This applies especially to Vitamin A, which guards against viruses and bacteria; Vitamin E, another protective vitamin; and Vitamin C which is involved in strengthening the immune system and preventing allergens passing through to the cell itself. The B vitamins are of prime importance, especially pantothenic acid. There have been cases where an allergy has cleared just by introducing pantothenic acid into the diet. However, if pathtothenic acid is taken in supplement form you should also take B complex with it for it to work most effectively.

Children who develop allergies often eat junk foods as a very large part of their diet – refined carbohydrates, fizzy drinks, sweets and chocolate. A child with a well-nourished, healthy body and a strong immune system is much less likely to suffer allergies. Stress – especially the stress of illness – can cause an allergic reaction in a child, which usually disappears after the illness is over. Another reason for keeping your child's immune system healthy and ensuring they do not contract an infection or an illness.

The difficulty of course is to diagnose food allergy. In fact, many people, children especially, have been labelled as anything from hypochondriacs to neurotics, when in reality they have been suffering from intolerance to something in their diet. If you should suspect your child to be allergic to something he eats, the wisest course would be to take him to a nutritionist because detecting a food allergy is a skilled task. Many doctors will use the Pulse Test, where the pulse is taken before eating and at 10, 20, 40 and 60 minutes after eating a food that is suspect. An increase in the pulse-rate, or a decrease even, could be a suspicious sign.

In the Sublingual Test, a very small amount of the suspected food is placed under the tongue, where it can be absorbed quickly into the bloodstream and may cause a fast reaction.

It is possible to experiment at home by excluding certain foods from the diet for a period of about two to three weeks and observing whether various symptoms cease. If they do then the food could be re-introduced and the reaction, if any, observed. A different food could be tried if the symptoms have not cleared.

An indication of a food allergy is craving for a certain food. If a child or adult claims that they cannot possibly give up a certain food, or really loves a certain food, it is a good idea to suspect an allergy to it.

Woman magazine reported on some cases of allergy in March 1987. Duncan, who had severe asthma, relied heavily on conventional medicines; when the whole family went on a raw, fresh food diet for three weeks, Duncan's asthma disappeared. That, of course, was a rigid diet which Duncan won't have to follow all the time. What he now does is avoid the junk food which was a major part of his diet.

Then there were Dick and John who were so hyperactive

they wrecked everything at nursery school. Orange squash, fish fingers and other foods with colourings and additives would trigger off their uncontrollable behaviour. Since more care has been taken with their diet, they are no longer the terrible twins that they were.

There was also the case of ten-year-old Caroline who suddenly started not wanting to go to school. Neither her parents nor her teacher and headmaster could find a reason. Caroline got worse, and also developed headaches, stomach upsets, and became very aggressive. Her teacher then asked the question which should always be asked if all possibilities have been explored: 'Could it possibly be due to something she's eating or drinking?'

Caroline's parents decided to write down everything she ate and drank, and her reaction to these items. They did this for three weeks and then it was the end of the school term. In a few days, they noticed that Caroline had certainly improved. It would have been very easy for her parents to have said at this stage that her problems were obviously stemming from a dislike of the school. But they were too wise to jump to conclusions hastily. They realized that their daughter's diet had changed during the holidays. Caroline had been taking packed lunches to school during the term – often it would be peanut butter sandwiches and orange squash to drink. These items just didn't happen to be on her menu during the holidays, so they re-introduced peanut butter and orange squash and her symptoms returned. They tried peanut butter on its own and Caroline was fine. So the culprit was orange drinks, not only squashes but plain orange juice as well. So, at long last, they realized that it was oranges in general which affected her.

A postscript to this happy ending was that the parents discovered cheese to be the item of food triggering off the unexplained sneezing bouts which Caroline's brother had suffered and which had been diagnosed as hay fever.

Yet another avenue to explore in the pursuit of complete well-being for your child is a condition known as Hypoglycaemia, or Low Blood Sugar. It is the opposite of hyperglycaemia which is too much sugar in the blood. Hypoglycaemia is having too little sugar in the blood and this can occur because too much refined sugar has been taken into the body. When there is too much refined sugar ingested, it is absorbed too quickly into the blood. When there is too much sugar in the blood, the hormone called insulin, manufactured by the pancreas, drives the sugar out of the blood into the body cells where it can be stored as glycogen, for future energy. It is stored in the liver and the muscles as well. From here it can be converted into fat unless it's used. The complication is that the pancreas, when it is called upon to release insulin to this extent, on a regular basis, learns to be trigger-happy and makes too good a job of it, so that the blood sugar is cleared out too rigorously and its level becomes too low in the blood.

In other words, when you eat sugar the excess is removed too efficiently, and you are left with too little sugar in the blood. Then you crave more sugar. This doesn't affect the body cells so much, but it does affect the cells of the brain because glucose, made into glycogen from the blood sugar, is required by the brain on a constant basis in constant amounts, if the brain is to function properly, so it is no use giving the brain glycogen in fits and starts. Also, when the level of sugar in the blood is low, the adrenal glands produce adrenalin and cortisone to help release stored glucose in the body cells, and this process is always stressful.

If glucose from blood sugar does not reach the nerve cells of the brain regularly, as glycogen, then all kinds of symptoms appear – physical symptoms and actual personality changes.

The physical symptoms and personality changes which can result if glucose is not available to the brain on a smooth and constant basis are numerous – dizziness, panic attacks, sweating, hunger, tiredness, shifts of mood, migraine and headaches. Low blood sugar can cause anxiety, nightmares, hyperactivity and depression. It can cause food cravings, allergic reactions, alcoholism and suicidal tendencies. Dawdling along, outbursts of irritability and bad temper could all be caused by low blood sugar.

There is varied opinion as to whether hypoglycaemia is a very commonplace syndrome displaying itself as many different symptoms, or whether it is an unusual condition. It is certain that its different symptoms can be caused by many other factors. But, because the symptoms can have other causes, low blood sugar is often unrecognized, with sometimes disastrous consequences – the child being labelled as a hypochondriac or a neurotic manufacturing imaginary illnesses for various reasons. Over forty years ago, a Dr Wilder in New York observed that low blood sugar produces mental symptoms that are characteristic of criminals, neurotics, and difficult and unbalanced people. Dr Wilder also found that low blood sugar caused a tendency to be negative and pessimistic, with difficulty in making decisions; that it slowed the mental processes and inhibited initiative. A child will often deny he has said something or done something, because he genuinely does not remember. Says Dr Wilder:

'In its simplest form, it is a tendency to deny everything, contradict everything, refuse everything at any price.'

Other researchers have confirmed Dr Wilder's observations.

If you do suspect your child to be hypoglycaemic, it is wisest to consult a doctor who will do a glucose tolerance test. Doctors who do this test on a regular basis find one in ten patients suffering from hypoglycaemia. The condition is certainly not rare, and there is sufficient evidence that it is increasing alarmingly.

The cause of hypoglycaemia is most definitely the modern Western diet with its refined foods, additives, preservatives and colourings in foods, and its high sugar content. All of these items can provide a temporary relief of symptoms but then cause an aggravation of the condition very shortly afterwards.

The treatment, and the prevention, of low blood sugar involves a regimen that every child would benefit from, regardless of whether you suspect hypoglycaemia or not.

1. The diet should contain as little as possible of the refined carbohydrates, sweets of all kinds, biscuits and cakes.

2. The diet should be high in protein, because protein foods raise the blood sugar and keep it high for a longer time than any other type of food.

3. A nutritious breakfast should be eaten before school. For a child to drink only a cup of coffee before school, as so many of my pupils do, is the road to disaster. In fact, it is important to cut out tea and coffee wherever possible.

4. Smaller meals, oftener, should be the rule rather than a

great interval between two or three meals. It is a good idea for a child with low blood sugar to eat snacks between meals. Nuts and seeds would be good – unsalted of course – whole fresh fruit or a glass of milk. Don't serve fruit juices – there is too much concentrated fructose, fruit sugar, in juice.

5. Rest is very important to children with low blood sugar; but so is physical exercise – as long as it is not too strenuous.

6. All the vitamins and minerals are important, especially the B Complex and Vitamin C; with the minerals calcium, magnesium, zinc, potassium and chromium. The B vitamins, B1, B3 and B5, with zinc and chromium, help to heal a pancreas which has been overworking.

But the one golden rule is, whether a youngster has low blood sugar or not, discourage the sugar. The less sugar you give your child, the less they will crave. I know you're up against it. Sugary treats and sweets are society's big bribes and big rewards. There are commercial pressures in the form of advertising; there are strategically-placed counters in supermarkets that lure a child to sweets, ice-cream, chocolate, soft drinks and chewing gum. There are parents and relatives who bribe and reward with sweets; and teachers at school who'll reward good work with a lollipop. Don't be discouraged. Stick to your principles and gradually cut out the amount of sugar your child consumes. Do not worry if this cannot be achieved quickly, a slow and steady reduction will still bring results.

CHAPTER 6
THE USE OF
SUPPLEMENTS

The question that many parents ask is should we provide vitamins and minerals in tablet form in case a youngster does not get enough from his or her usual range of foods?

My answer is, most definitely, YES. Yes, it is an excellent idea to provide your child with a naturally formed, correctly balanced multi-vitamin and mineral supplement bought from a reputable manufacturer. I am a fervent believer in supplementing a child's diet – and an adult's diet as well – with tablets or capsules containing natural vitamins and minerals. I've proved it myself, and with my family, that these additional quotas of nutrients are extremely beneficial in the promotion of all-round mental and physical well-being, and I have also had the opportunity to measure the effect of a supplement on groups of children whom I teach. I would never hesitate to recommend it, but I would stress – not as a substitute for nutritious food; not as a 'lazy way out' of providing a good diet, but working with the diet to provide the very optimum health.

Why? Because, firstly, we do not live in a nutritionally ideal world. Ideally, we should be getting all our nutrients from the food we eat, as our ancestors did, but unless you grow and rear your own food organically, well-away from any pollution of the air, the water and the soil, then this is not possible.

Frozen, canned and packeted foods, together with a more refined diet means that much of our food has been robbed of vital nutrients. Additives, colourings and preservatives are found in many food-stuffs; extra nutrients are needed to counteract their harmful effects, plus the fact that the more removed these foods are from their live, natural state, the fewer are the vitamins and minerals contained in them. The soils of our country are often worn out soils and do not produce foods rich in the nutrients we need. Pesticides and chemical fertilizers used to encourage crops, apart from being highly suspect to health, destroy many vitamins that plants should contain. So it is with chemicals used in the processing of foods – they lower the vitamin and mineral content of foods as well. Refined bread and cereals cannot possibly provide an adequate range of the B and E vitamins. Fruits and vegetables brought across country or imported from a foreign country are picked before they have ripened so that they don't get rotten, but they have nowhere near the vitamin and mineral content of homegrown, freshly-picked foods. In fact, the nutritive value of most food begins to fall as soon as it is picked or harvested, especially the vitamins A and C found mainly in fruit and vegetables.

Other enemies of nutrients are the heat used in cooking and direct contact with water for soaking and cooking. Vitamin C is soluble in water, as are all the B vitamins. Contact with light, rough handling and storage also detrimentally affect vitamin potency. Freshness of a food, remember, goes hand in hand with its nutritive value.

There is another factor we have to contend with in modern times which is a great thief of vitamins and minerals – and that is stress. Anyone under stress needs a far greater supply of vitamins and minerals, especially the B's, and of course children are under constant stress, as there is pressure on them to perform well at school, to work towards examinations and a career, apart from the traumas of adolescence itself and the usual problems of adjusting to the adult world.

Stress as well, or an illness, or an emotional upset, will cause a normally good eater to reject food. Not eating the same amount as usual, however nutritious the meal may be, will leave your child short of vitamins and minerals. I cannot think of any of the youngsters I know who retain a hearty appetite at test time or examination time therefore, obviously, the usual level of vitamins and minerals are not present in the body.

Some teenage girls are obsessed with dieting and to cut down on food without the provision of nutrients from elsewhere is a very dangerous habit at any age. Extreme tiredness also, from a mentally and physically demanding day at school, will blunt the appetite of a youngster, and a carefully prepared meal will be left half-eaten.

As parents, too, we have got to accept the fact that the older the child, the less control we have over his or her eating habits. Meals at school nowadays are mostly cafeteria style and most conscientious parents cannot check at lunch time whether their child has had a plateful of chips, a doughnut and a fizzy drink, or whether they chose wholemeal salad roll, with natural fruit bar or fresh fruit to follow. Giving a multi-vitamin and mineral supplement with breakfast or the evening meal – it's better to take supplements with a meal – will ensure that omitted vitamins are provided.

There is no getting away from the fact, either, that children of all ages love chocolates, sweets, biscuits and cakes. Yes, you can educate their tastes, get them to cut down on sweet and sugary junk, and point out to them the inestimable benefits of avoiding too much of this type of carbohydrate. There is no-one, child or adult, who does not fall into nutritional temptation at some time or another. Even the best trained child will occasionally opt for a chocolate bar rather than a packet of raisins or dates, especially when they're with friends or at a party. To digest a pure form of carbohydrate like chocolate the body needs to draw upon its supply of vitamins. Without a supplement can you guarantee that there are enough nutrients left for your child's needs?

I must emphasize that the way to supplement the diet wisely is to use a natural – rather than a synthetic – vitamin and mineral supplement, one which contains a wide range of nutrients and which has been produced by a reputable manufacturer. I would emphasize, too, that it is unwise to give large doses of separate vitamins or minerals as this would cause an imbalance of vitamins and minerals in the body. It is a good balance of all the nutrients that the body needs.

A vitamin and mineral supplement is entirely safe. It isn't a drug and can never have the adverse effects that some medicinal drugs cause.

So, to come to my own experiments in nutrition with my pupils at Darland School. I chose this assignment to try to discover for myself whether the junk food diet of many of my pupils, deficient as it was in many vitamins and minerals, was affecting their thought processes – their memory, concentration and their overall performance in school, as well as their attitude and behaviour, and whether providing vitamins and minerals in tablet form would make any difference. I would really have preferred to have altered their eating habits, but this would have been difficult to monitor and control, and would have been a long-term study for which I did not then have sufficient time.

The only trouble with this trial I wanted to conduct was that I had no vitamin and mineral supplements to give to my pupils on a daily basis, and for long enough for the trial to be effective. I couldn't possibly afford to go and buy so many out of my own pocket. The solution was to write a begging letter to all the major manufacturers of natural, additive-free supplements, outlining what I wished to do and asking them would they like to sponsor me by providing the vitamin and mineral tablets. Some polite refusals began to arrive by post, but one morning there did come a letter I wanted, from Dr Robert Woodward of Larkhall Laboratories in Putney.

Larkhall Laboratories are well-established health supplement manufacturers whose products are pure and natural without synthetic or chemical additives. Yes, Larkhall would be delighted to sponsor such an experiment and I could have as many vitamin and mineral tablets as I needed. I was delighted and got down to planning my trial.

I used a class of thirty second year pupils of mixed ability, which I felt was the most suitable and convenient group.

My group were perfectly normal children from an ordinary school – that is if there is any such phenomenon as a normal child and an ordinary school.

Anyway, this class of thirty children was divided into three groups. Ten children took a multi-vitamin and mineral tablet, ten took a placebo, a dummy tablet, and the other ten did not take anything at all. They were the control group. Twenty pupils then reported every day, after lunch, to take their tablets, and they were supplied with sufficient tablets for weekends and the half-term holiday.

It was a double-blind trial – neither the pupils nor myself knew who were taking the 'real' supplement and who were taking the dummy ones.

All tests and questionnaires were completed by pupils at

the start of the trial in September 1985, and all of these were repeated twelve weeks later, at the end of the trial.

The tablets used in the trial were based on the original *Trufree* brand manufactured by Larkhall under the name of *Tandem*, and contained a wide spectrum of the essential vitamins and minerals. However, I decided to modify the original formula and increase substantially the amounts of vitamin C, vitamins B3 and B5, and added a little more chromium. Vitamin C is such an important vitamin – it helps children to cope with stress as well as strengthen their immune systems, and it also enchances the absorption of iron, and prevents the destruction of folic acid in foods. Vitamin B3 and chromium help cope with the large amounts of sugar many children consume, and vitamin B5 also helps in coping with stress.

The whole class had compiled diet profiles for me before the trial started, keeping an account of everything they ate for three days. I had expected to be somewhat shocked by these profiles but I had never dreamt they would be so bad. Half of the children never bothered with breakfast and just had a coffee with two or three sugars. Their lunches were usually chips followed by something like a doughnut. What was so appalling about their diet was not the meals they had at home but the extra between-meal snacks of cakes, sweets, ice-lollies, chocolates, crisps and so on which were consumed so regularly.

The results were very interesting. The group taking the supplements showed an average increase of 6.4 points in their IQ compared with 3.0 points for the placebo group and 3.3 for the control.

The questions on the parent and teacher questionnaires were assessed on a 1 to 5 point scale and were intended to indicate any changes in the child's behaviour. At the completion of the trial, responses were compared and indicated either a positive or negative trend. These figures show the results.

	Supplement	Placebo	Control
Parent questionnaire	+5	—7	—2
Teacher questionnaire	+9	—4	—3

So it is obvious that, despite the rather short duration of the trial, there is a significant increase in the average IQ of the group taking the supplements compared with the other two groups. There is also a positive trend towards the supplemented group as indicated by the results of the parent and teacher questionnaires.

It is most interesting to note that the two larger increases in IQ, both of 15 points, appeared in the two pupils who were on extremely poor diets, the two who consumed the largest quantities of stimulants, refined carbohydrates, and fizzy drinks.

The results of this pilot trial were sufficiently interesting to encourage me to think about a more sophisticated study, involving a much greater number of children. I had no problem with sponsors this time, but I preferred to keep to my initial benefactor.

This larger trial involved 90 second year pupils whose parents consented to let them participate, and the rest of the second year acted as the control group. I eliminated as far as was humanly possibly any factors such as difference in sex, background or ability which might prejudice the final results. Every pupil completed a three-day diet profile which was then computer analysed to show any imbalances and any vitamin and mineral deficiencies. The trial started in September 1986, and was completed in June 1987. Before beginning the supplementation, the following tests and questionnaires were completed; they were also completed again at the finish of the trial.

Non-verbal IQ test
Cognitive abilities test – three parts
Rutter: behaviour scale (teachers)
Behaviour questionnaire (teachers)
Behaviour questionnaire (parents)

A computer programme to test powers of concentration was carried out on all pupils at the start, mid-way and at the end of the study, and the Harrell memory test was conducted at intervals through the period of the trial.

Dr David Benton, of the Psychology Department at the University of Swansea, monitored the issuing of the placebos and supplements and carried out all statistical analyses of the findings. These were published in *The Lancet* of 23

January 1988, and the results were very exciting. *The Lancet*'s summary reported that the supplement group, but not the placebo group or the remaining 30 who took no tablets, showed a significant increase in non-verbal intelligence. The trial was also featured in the BBC's QED programme 'Your Child's Diet on Trial' on 20 January 1988.

I'll sum up my attitude to supplements with an extract from an interview I gave to Anne Kent for *Mother* magazine.

'Mr Roberts said he realized it would have been better to try to change the children's eating habits rather than give them pills, but the problem was that such changes can take many years. However, he has found that the publicity given to the experiment has made parents and pupils much more aware of the value of eating well. He has started a healthier eating campaign in the school aimed at showing the children the positive advantages. For example, they will do better at lessons and sport and have better skins.'

Part IV
WHAT HAPPENS AT SCHOOL

Chapter 1.
Questions for parents

Chapter 2.
How a school is run

Chapter 3.
The primary choice

Chapter 4.
Choosing a secondary school

Chapter 5.
Invitations to take up

Chapter 6.
The new exams

CHAPTER 1
QUESTIONS FOR PARENTS

1. Can you recognize a good school?
2. Can you recognize a good teacher? Not the popular one but possibly the strict one who keeps nagging for homework.
3. If your child is of school age, have you regularly visited the school?
4. Have you been regularly invited to your child's school, for whatever reason?
5. If you had a minor problem about your child's schooling – poor handwriting; someone teasing them; seemingly not enough homework; – could you approach the school with confidence, and would you know who to contact?
6. If you had a major problem – school phobia; poor reports; suspected truancy; bullying; suspected glue-sniffing; – could you approach the school with confidence?
7. Are you confident that your child is being well-taught by experts, in all subjects?
8. If your child is now in Primary School, are you aware that you can state a preference for a particular Secondary School in your area, and are you confident that you could make the right choice?
9. Do you have a general idea of how the new GCSE examinations affect your child?
10. Are you completely happy about the school your child attends and the way they are being educated? Is your child as happy about it as you are?

If all your answers to these questions are 'yes', then you are in a most enviable position indeed. I have met very few parents who have been able to do so.

It is so important for your child to attend a good school –

at primary and secondary level. For a start, it will complement the excellence of the home. It will prepare your youngster for life, and will help in the process of integration into society so that they become a valuable member of it, and will make their own individual contribution. There will be other children there to speak to, play with, learn to share facilities with, sing and act with, learn consideration for, identify with, argue with, play games with, share responsibility with, gain experience of the differing range of other personalities, and exercise self-discipline. All this, apart from being taught, hopefully, by qualified specialist teachers who'd be experts in their own disciplines.

'The quality of the primary school is more important in terms of pupil achievement than the home background',

claims *Nursery World* of 24 April 1986, reporting about the Inner London Education Authority's four year research into primary education. I must quote as well, of course, what they still claim about your role: 'However, parental involvement still proved to be extremely important, both in the classroom and at home.'

So it's you two working together – parent and school – which will create the kind of excellence that every child, without exception, is capable of in one avenue or another. Finding an excellent school often demands of the parent a great deal of perseverance, insistence and know-how. But once you find such a school, you'll certainly recognize the effect it will have on your child's attitude and progress.

I must point out of course that in some areas, certainly in cities and large towns, there could be a choice of quite a few schools. In other areas, the choice might be limited to as few as two schools.

Where there is a choice, I'll guide you into making the best; where there isn't, then I'll show you how to make the most of what's available.

So how do concerned parents find the best school for their son or daughter, and how do they get involved with that school to gain the best advantage for their child? Before I present you with guidelines, it is vital for you to know how a secondary school is organized and run.

CHAPTER 2
HOW A SCHOOL IS RUN

We must take the headmaster or headmistress as the focal point of any school. In a secondary school, what goes on around the Headteacher is much more complicated than at primary level, where there might be a Head and one Deputy, and probably no more than half a dozen classroom teachers at most.

In a large secondary comprehensive school of about a thousand pupils the staff next in importance to the Head would be two or three Deputy Headteachers. They would have a minimal teaching commitment in whatever subject they had specialized, and the rest of their duties would be supportive to the Head's role of organizer, administrator and decision-maker.

Next in importance would be the Senior Teachers, who perform some of the major tasks that need specific attention and expertise, such as Assessment Techniques, Profiling, Career Guidance or Curriculum Development, terms which will be explained later. These teachers would have quite a substantial teaching commitment in whatever was their specialist subject. So, the 'senior management' team of a large school would consist of the Headteacher, the Deputy Headteachers and the Senior Teachers. This group would be the one that would discuss medium and long-term planning in matters of policy and administration.

In a secondary school of eight hundred or more pupils, where there is a wide range of subjects offered, there operates what is usually termed The Faculty System. The school is divided, subject wise, into Faculties, with a Head of Faculty in charge; ideally, a well-experienced graduate who has proven herself or himself to be a teacher of excellence and dedication.

This Faculty Head, then, would be in sole charge of the day-to-day running of the classes within their domain, and would be responsible for co-ordinating the academic work of all the subjects within that faculty.

This is a typical division of a secondary school into Faculties.

1. Faculty of Languages and Communication,

where the usual subjects taught are English; English Literature; Media Studies; Music; Drama; French; German. In some schools additional languages may also be offered.

2. Faculty of Mathematics,

where the usual subjects are Mathematics, Computer Studies and Statistics.

3. Faculty of Science,

where the subjects would be Physics; Chemistry; Biology; Combined Science and Rural Studies.

4. Faculty of Humanities,

possibly *and Commerce,* where there would be a very wide range of subjects: from the more traditional Geography; History; Religious Education; and Social Studies to the more recently devised courses such as Integrated Humanities; Understanding Industrial Society; or Community Studies. This faculty might also include Commerce; Business Studies; and Office Practice. It can also include Physical Education.

5. The Faculty of Design

would include such subjects as Home Economics; Needle-work; Homecraft; Child Care; and Art, along with the more

recent ones such as Landscape Gardening; Building
Construction and Maintenance; Electronics; and Graphical
Communication.

Within the Faculty, under the overall jurisdiction of the
Faculty Head, there would be Heads of Departments, in
charge of their respective subjects, and possibly two or three
subject teachers.

Pupils in the first year of their secondary education would
not, of course, be offered this wide a choice of subjects. In
fact, there would be no choice at all at this stage. A typical
timetable for new entrants would be: five lessons of English;
five lessons of Maths; five lessons of Science; four lessons of
Design; four lessons of Humanities; four lessons of French;
four lessons of P.E.; three lessons of Music and in Wales four
lessons of Welsh. Another one lesson might be taken up with
learning the skills of using the Library efficiently; and
another one or two lessons might include what some
schools call Personal and Social Development. This PSD
Course is designed to help pupils adjust to all stages of
school life and the problems accompanying these various
stages. It would include Health Education and the
development of good social and emotional relationships. All
in all, the first year timetable would emphasise a well-
balanced course of study.

So, the *academic* division of a school is into Faculties and
Departments. There is another way in which a school is 'split
up' – into *Pastoral* divisions – so that the pupil can be cared
for and guided in a broader sense than merely academic.
This division is sometimes made according to year groups.
There is a Head of Year, also referred to as the Year Tutor, for
every year in the school – Head of First Year; Head of Second
Year, and so on, who is responsible for every facet of a child's
welfare in that year. Problem-solving, usually of the
behavioural or personal kind, is the speciality of the Year
Head. It is he or she who will usually contact parents by
letter or telephone if there is a problem, and it is the Year
Head who is in close contact with the Educational Social
Worker and the external support agencies. The Year Head
directs the Year Team of Form Tutors and co-ordinates their
tasks, sets the tone and establishes the morale of the team.

I would advise any parent with a problem about their

child to contact the Head of Year or Head of House unless the problem is very minor, in which case the Form Tutor could be contacted. Many parents are very reluctant to get in touch with the school unless the matter is really serious, by which time it could be too late. Don't hesitate to contact school, however trivial you think the problem is. Teachers need and welcome your communication. The Form Tutor has responsibility for registering pupils before morning and afternoon lessons, and is in charge of the general organization of this group, such as their conduct; regularity in handing in homework; issuing of timetables; or issuing any information they should receive. The Form Tutor is the first point of reference when dealing with a pupil, and the first link in the chain of Pastoral Care.

The timetable discussed previously will give you an idea of the kind of curriculum your child would follow in the first year of secondary school. Curriculum means the whole range of subjects which is offered in a school. Take a look at your child's timetable and ask them to explain it to you. Ask about the different subjects and the various members of staff; ask which subjects are enjoyable and those which might present a few problems. In fact, discussing the timetable with your child is an excellent way to communicate. You will soon get to know which are their favourite days and which are the not too enjoyable ones, and you can sympathize accordingly.

In the second and third year, your child's curriculum would change, but only slightly, the change depending mostly on whether they would be taught in mixed ability groups or in sets.

The very important change of curriculum occurs in the fourth year, in readiness for the two-year course leading to external examinations at the end of the fifth year. An external examination is one which is set and marked by an examining body outside school. All examinations a child will sit before the fifth year will be internal examinations compiled and marked by the subject specialists who teach them.

The curriculum your child will have followed in the first three years at secondary school is designed to provide good, general education. It would not be possible to continue all the subjects of the first three years into the fourth and fifth, to a standard required for examinations, so choices have to be made. There will still be subjects which are compulsory: English; Maths; Religious Education; Physical Education; and Careers. These are often referred to as *'core'* subjects of the curriculum. In addition to these your child will choose others which are *'optional'* normally another six. The school will present your child with six groups of subjects and they will choose one from each of the groups. They will get plenty of opportunity to discuss their choice with the subject teachers, and also with a Senior Teacher who would be in charge of the overall management of option choices, and who would be available to parents as well if they wished to discuss their child's option choices with a specialist. A school would normally encourage a choice of at least one science subject; at least one Humanities; one Design; and another three from a number of other subjects that would not fit into any of those groups. Even with options, the desirability of an allround choice of subjects is emphasized.

I would stress that your child should choose their option subjects very carefully, for the right rather than for the wrong reasons, and that you should point this out quite strongly. The wrong reasons for choosing a subject are: that friends are choosing it; or that they have always got on with the teacher taking this subject. Teachers can, and do, change jobs and in any event, that particular teacher might not, for administrative reasons, be taking the particular group your child is in.

Really, choices should be made with your child's career in mind. There is no problem if a pupil has an idea about what they want to do. A doctor or a vet must have physics, chemistry and biology; a physiotherapist must have physics, and so on. The careers specialist in the school will give advice about specific subjects for specific careers. Most schools have a careers room, or a careers section in the library where booklets and pamphlets about various careers, and the prospectuses of various colleges and universities are available. These would give details of all courses offered and which examinations and grades are needed to gain admission. Many schools, too, or groups of schools together, hold a Careers Convention, to which leading business and professional people are invited to talk to pupils and parents, and to answer their queries.

If your child at this stage has no idea what they would like to do, then it is more difficult to make choices. In this event, choosing as wide a range of subjects as possible is the best idea. Also, if your child really excels at a subject, they could opt for this one and then explore its career prospects.

CHAPTER 3
THE PRIMARY CHOICE

The role of the primary school is a vitally important role in the educative process of our children. There might be parents reading this book who wish to choose a primary school for their young child; whose son or daughter, might be just starting primary school, or might be at different stages of primary schooling.

A major study of junior schools in the Inner London area has recently been published which identifies the factors that make one school better than another in terms of academic development and behaviour. The project followed the progress of two thousand children from the age of seven until they transferred to secondary school at age eleven; they were drawn from fifty schools from across the whole authority.

The project is all about school effectiveness and how to measure it. The study found that a primary school had a high chance of being a good school if

1. it combined the infant and junior age range,
2. there were not more than 160 children in the Junior section ,
3. the classes were no more than 24 in number,
4. the school was 'voluntary-aided', meaning that it is run by a religious denomination, who would be partly responsible for funding the school with the local authority, and who would control the appointment of teachers and the kind of religious instruction given,
5. the school had a good environment and few upheavals in the form of change of teachers, or building work,

6. it had a headteacher who had been in the school for between three and seven years.

According to the report there are several other important factors which help to ensure the success of a school:

1. The dedication and understanding of the headteacher and deputy.
2. Stimulating, enthusiastic teachers who are consistent in their methods of teaching and who give the children basic grounding in the three R's.
3. The organisation of the pupils' work by the teacher rather than giving the pupils unlimited choice from a list of tasks,
4. A high degree of industry amongst the children in a noise and movement level that was not excessive.
5. Teachers who used opportunities to talk to the class as a whole rather than concentrating purely on individual teaching. In other words, an effective teacher will have a variety of styles of teaching, and be neither too traditionally authoritarian nor too progressively child-centred.
6. The belief amongst the head and the staff that parents should be encouraged to help children with their school tasks and involve themselves in the activities of the classroom.

You cannot fail if you apply some or all of these guidelines, in your search and assessment of a primary school.

CHAPTER 4
CHOOSING A SECONDARY SCHOOL

How do you go about evaluating and choosing a secondary school for your child? Many schools nowadays have to do what they have never done ever before, and that is to 'sell' their 'product', with headteachers naturally assuming the role of chief salesperson.

What areas of school policy and organization should you investigate when you visit a school with a view to 'purchasing' it for your child?

1. First of all, before visiting any school, you should send to each one for a prospectus or handbook. Such a booklet would probably contain a message from the headteacher; information about the development of the school; subjects on the curriculum and the choice of subjects; staff structure; advice to parents about contacting school; arrangements for parents' evenings and open evenings; rules about school uniform; discipline policy; school clubs, and so on. Not every handbook will contain the same type of information, but every one should be very informative about most aspects of the school.

2. Having studied the handbook, you should make an appointment to see the headteacher at each school – not a deputy or a Head of Year. It's important for you to speak to the Head personally. A Headteacher makes or breaks a school by determining the standards, the tone, the quality, the ethos of a school; that elusive component which is so difficult to define: that aura of excellence about a school which is so difficult to achieve, but so recognizable when it is achieved. It is the personality and conviction of the Head which is the determining factor in the real excellence of a

school. How can you judge what he or she is like? Almost impossible, at first glance. If it's possible then go and listen to them speak – to a parents' meeting for example – and then talk to other people. What do parents think about them? If you know any of the staff at the school ask their opinion because they are the ones who'll really know what a Head is like.

3. When you make your appointment with the Head, you must be very specific about what time you would like your visit to be. The ideal time is about ten o'clock in the morning: you'll be chatting to the Head for ten or fifteen minutes, and then you'll be taken on a tour of the school which will take you into the mid-morning break that most schools have around 10.15 or 10.30 a.m., at the latest 10.45 a.m. Make a note of pupil behaviour in the corridors. Did the children give way to you and the Head or did they walk through you and trample you underfoot? Did they seem unruly? Were they running and shouting wildly? Did anyone open a door for you? Were you wading knee-deep in crisp-papers and apple-cores? Were there groups of stragglers hanging around the corridors after the bell for end of break had rung? Did the school seem to take a long time to 'settle' after the end of break? In other words, is the Headteacher running a 'tight ship', or are things rather lax and disorganized?

You can tell the Head quite openly why you chose your time to view the school, and you can be quite open about what you're looking for. It may raise a few eyebrows, but they will certainly respect your keenness and will want you as a parent. Keen and caring parents are extremely valuable commodities, due to the simple fact that their children are bound to do well in school.

4. Make inquiries about the standard of behaviour and discipline in the school. You can't ask a Head directly what school discipline is like. There are a few questions you can put though:

(a) What happens to the handful of pupils that you get in every school who are troublemakers? Don't let them tell you there aren't any. The best answer you could get here is that, if a child has a behavioural problem, then the parents are asked to come into school for the beginning of what would be a thorough discussion and counselling regime, so that no stone is left unturned in the attempt to modify the child's behaviour. Possibly a careful eye would be kept on a disruptive pupil through a system of lesson reports which a child would carry with him to every lesson, and which he would show to his Year Tutor and parents at the end of the day. This is a most effective monitoring method which deters many a child from bad behaviour. What you are looking for is a well-considered system of sanctions and deterrents in the school, and, of course, these deterrents do work in the case of the vast majority of pupils.

(b) Tell the Head that you've read a teachers' union booklet called *Pupil Violence and Serious Disorders in Schools.* You can get a copy free from the Education Centre, Birmingham. I'll give you some quotations from the pamphlet. Ask the Head if anything resembling this occurs at their school.

'Stabbing – pupil to pupil, knife-throwing, pupil thrown over high balcony, pupil thrown through plate glass window'
(*Church of England high school, Lancashire.*)

'Staff... confronted with foul abusive language, and threats of violence.'
(*Church of England school, Birmingham.*)

'Office gutted by fire started by three pupils. Damage amounted to £10,000.'
(*Comprehensive, Cleveland.*)

'Car tyre slashed while on school property in working hours. Nails placed in staff car park. Bonnet of car walked over. Bottles placed under car tyre. Valves removed from car tyres during parents' evening.'
(*High School, Cheshire.*)

Are these isolated and exaggerated incidents? We have to face the facts: they're not. *The Sunday Times* of 9 November 1986, reports that

'two recent reports in education publications have detailed the concern of primary school staff about the increase in violent behaviour in children as young as five: foul-mouthed, bullying, spitting and kicking. In one incident, it took three adults to restrain a seven-year-old having a tantrum. In one day, from a group of 587 primary teachers, 312 seriously disruptive incidents were reported.'

Ask the Head what his or her views are on the teaching of moral education and good behaviour in the school.

(c) Ask the Head if they use the cane. Not that I believe that whether they do or not is of tremendous significance, but you need to know.

(d) Ask the Head whether a disruptive child who impedes the progress of the class your child is in would be excluded from that class, or would the teacher and the other children have to put up with him?

(e) Ask the Head how strong are all the links in the pastoral care chain. It's not enough for your own child to be well-behaved and attentive; all the others in the group must be as well, or maximum learning will not take place.

(f) Find out from the Head what methods are used for dealing with unacceptable behaviour. Don't go to school breathing fire if your child has been kept in for detention at lunch-time; or is asked to go around school picking up litter; is given lines or an essay on the topic of his misbehaviour; or forbidden to go on a school outing because of some misdemeanour. You should always find out what sanctions are used in a school *before* you send your child there. If there are none I'd be inclined to advise you to keep *very* well away!

5. Ask the Head for a copy of the results of external examinations, in every subject, for the past five years. You could ask for these when you're writing or calling for the prospectus. It is now obligatory for every school to make available their results to anyone who wishes to study them. Compare them with the examination results of the other schools you're considering. You can't go on results alone, but every parent wishes their child to do well in Fifth and Sixth Year examinations. You need a school for your child that takes examination results very seriously.

Ask what the pass rates are in the important areas of English, Maths and Science.

I believe that you need to look most carefully of all at the

English results of a school. Your child needs the skills of English above all others. Without being able to write and speak, without being able to discuss topics and put forward their point of view clearly and fluently, without being able to read a wide variety of written material with understanding and sensitivity, and without being able to listen attentively in a variety of situations, your child cannot possibly be a high flyer in any career. English is *the* crucial subject. If there doesn't seem to be a strong and flourishing English department, then avoid the school at all costs. You could check, too, whether there's a Debating Society, a Drama Group, a Public Speaking Group, or a Book Society – all connected really with the vital skills of the English department.

You could, at this stage inquire what other extra-curricular activities are offered. Many schools will have clubs ranging from Chess to Orienteering, from Electronic Games to Christian Fellowship. Encourage your child to join at least one club because it is of tremendous value to a child in the process of integrating, developing pride in their school, and getting to know staff and other pupils on a personal level.

Ask the Head if the school has a policy of training pupils for examinations from an early age. Some schools have a policy of holding internal examinations only for fourth and fifth years, while others make a point of setting examinations from the first year. There is a lot to be said for early training, nerveracking though it is for first year pupils. It gives them the feel of examinations and it brings home to them that before examinations there needs to be a period of revision of all the work they've covered.

6. What a parent certainly needs to ask the Head is what degree of communication the school has with the home. Are you regularly invited to school for parents' evenings; open evenings; parent-teacher functions; school performances? Do you get the impression that the Head is really keen to get parents into school? Would you be welcome in school at any time? For whatever reason? Could you make an appointment to come to school on the very day that there is an urgent problem, or would you have to wait a few days? How soon would the school get in touch with you if your child had been discovered playing truant, or had been caught

smoking, had been insolent to a teacher or had become disruptive in class? Is there a 'homework' letter that would arrive if your child wasn't submitting work, or getting into the habit of being late handing in work? Many schools give every pupil a homework timetable, and it is worth checking that any specified homework is actually being set.

It is of paramount importance that the school recognizes that your role of parent is vital, and that it considers it a high priority to communicate and liaise with you.

7. You need to inquire about the standard of academic teaching in the school. You can hardly ask the Head: 'Are all your staff excellent teachers?', but you can ask whether all subjects are taught by teachers who are qualified to teach that particular subject.

Ask if you may speak to the Head of the Maths Faculty. This is a perfectly reasonable request and the Head and the Maths specialist will recognize your intelligent and caring concern. There's no point in your being an excellent parent if the teaching that your child receives at school is inferior. Your main query will be whether all the staff in the Maths department actually are mathematics specialists. Request a visit to the Science Laboratories. Are they well-equipped and well-organized? Perhaps you could have a chance to speak to the Head of Science and maybe see some practical experiments being conducted! If you have a daughter, ask the Science Head whether they have a policy of specifically encouraging girls to take the Science subjects. There are tremendous opportunities nowadays for girls in Science, but the old traditional idea of girls taking the Arts subjects and boys the Sciences, really dies hard. It is important to indoctrinate girls with different ideas about Science and to encourage them at an early age if they show any aptitude and ability.

8. Ask how large the classes are, certainly in English and Maths; and usually option subjects will have smaller groups. The advantages your child would get in a smaller class range from the obvious one of more individual attention from the teacher, to the more intangible ones of better teacher attitude and morale.

9. What kind of report will you get of your child's progress?

How often will you get a report? In the schools of this area, every child gets a booklet, twice a year, where there is a report page for every subject, with space not just for marks and grades, but for detailed comment which can extend to other pages if necessary. The back cover is detachable for the parent to sign, as proof that the report has been received; it has space as well for parent comment or request for discussion of the report with a teacher, the Head of Year/House, or Headteacher, if the parent wishes. Not all parents make a comment, but it is a good idea to do so and much appreciated by the Form Tutor.

10. Ask about school lunches. Is there a policy of healthy eating in the school, and an effort to keep the meals free of additives, colour, flavour and preservatives? Are there salads and wholemeal bread and rolls? Is the pastry for pies and pizzas wholemeal? Are the drinks pure fruit drinks? Are there fresh fruit and fresh vegetables? What about the Tuck Shop at mid-morning? Is it nutritionless and 'artificial', or are there items which will enable your child to work at peak performance from 10.15 a.m. to lunchtime?

By now, you will have given yourself – and no doubt the Head – something to think about. You have shown your real concern for your child's education and should now have all the information needed to help you decide if this is *the* school to develop your child's potential to the full, and the one where you're sure your child would be happy.

CHAPTER 5
INVITATIONS TO TAKE UP

'I didn't want to see you about anything in particular, Mr Roberts, but I wanted Andrea to know I'd been to see you.'

'I came just to check that Alan was still keeping up in Physics.'

These are typical opening sentences on Parents' Evening by parents whom I would have known before and possibly spoken to on many occasions. They're the parents of some of my best pupils, most of them very motivated parents who have changed the course of their youngsters' lives. They are parents who want to communciate with school; they want to help in the process of educating their children; they know it's a two-way process between school and home and they want to give all the support they can. A youngster rarely goes wrong with this kind of parent. If they do, it can soon be put right before things have gone too far.

Never refuse an opportunity of visiting your child's school, if at all possible. You'll know what's going on if you do, and your youngster will know that you know what's going on. The staff will recognize you as a keen and caring parent and will make a note of it.

These are the main functions at a secondary school which you would be invited to attend.

1. Parents' Evening

This is when you will be formally invited to school on a set evening to discuss your child's progress with all the members of staff who teach your child.

Take your child's report along with you, and take your child as well if you can.

Take the opportunity to ask about anything that concerns you; schoolwork, homework, behavioural problems or just seeking reassurance that your child is coping as well as everyone else. Whatever grievance you might have, whatever problem needs to be cleared up, always be polite. You'll achieve far more with reasonable discussion. If you feel that this grievance is not being handled, discussed and resolved thoroughly enough, then you'll have to go elsewhere. During Parents' Evening, the Head of Year/House, one of the Deputies, and the Headteacher, are available for consultation. If there happens to be too much demand on their time that evening, ring school in the morning, and make an appointment.

2. Open Evenings

are held by many schools for the parents of new pupils. They are usually held before the start of the September term.

At Open Evening, members of staff will meet parents and show them around school in small groups, explaining the set-up and the facilities, and answering any queries. It's a very good time to ask any pressing question or inform a teacher of any problem.

Open Evenings are an opportunity to get acquainted with your youngster's school, to feel the atmosphere, to show your face and display your interest. It can be a basis for very natural communication between you and your child.

3. The Parent Teacher Association

or PTA, is found in most schools and is a mixture of teachers and parents of a school, meeting at certain pre-arranged times. The aims of the PTA are generally to initiate activities which support the school in one way or another; it extends social relationships between the staff and parents and it acts as a fund-raising team.

Joining your PTA – to which you will automatically be invited – means becoming involved in a very practical way with the welfare of the school and the education of your own child. You will be involved in activities, the results of which are very real and tangible.

If it is not possible for you to belong to the PTA, you could always support some of their activities. One of the advantages of doing this is that you will come into contact with other parents, and in the course of conversation with them, it is amazing how much 'unofficial' information you will get about school.

4. Choice of subjects

is one of the most important meetings that you can attend. Towards the end of the third year, in preparation for the final years, pupils are given guidance about choice of subjects which will help them follow a chosen or possible career, and for which they show an aptitude. Apart from their compulsory core subjects, pupils usually choose one subject from each of six option groups. Most schools invite parents into school to discuss 'options', and on every school staff there is a Senior Teacher who deals with any queries from pupils and parents.

5. Profiles meetings

are similar to options meetings, and sometimes even held hand in hand. A profile is a document, varying in content and detail from school to school, which is designed to assess non-academic areas, or areas not covered by examinations. It covers such matters as the pupil's ability to form relationships, with adults and their own age group; capacity for leadership; concern for others and for the community; whether they are well-mannered, confident, trustworthy. Comments would also be made on participation in extra-curricular activities – clubs, societies, trips and visits and whether they have made a notable contribution to school life in general as well as pursuing academic qualifications.

One of the purposes of a profile is to motivate pupils by involving them in their own educational progress, and assessing areas of strength which would not normally be taken into account in any other document.

Ask at the Meeting, or at the PTA, whether these profiles are available for parents to read, before the final drafting of it is completed and your child brings it home. Is there an opportunity for you, the one who knows your child best, to contribute? Bear in mind that a well-compiled profile can make an impression on an employer, or a college principal, and could be one of the most important documents your child possesses.

6. Social Events

are among the most pleasant for parents to get involved in. There is plenty of opportunity at Christmas, Harvest Festival, the School Concert and sporting fixtures. Do go along if you can. The atmosphere at such functions is tremendous and teachers will know which parents support the school and take an active interest in its activities. This alone will benefit your child enormously. Again it will provide a bond between you, a subject for humour and interchange of ideas and comments. It will show that you care about this tremendously exciting process of education that is happening to your youngster, and that you want to be as involved as you can in it.

CHAPTER 6
THE NEW EXAMS

From 1988 onwards, when your child gets to be 16, if you live in England, Wales or Northern Ireland they will be sitting an entirely new examination. What we've known as 'O' Level GCE examinations and CSE examinations will now disappear. In their place is the new General Certificate of Secondary Education that we call the GCSE.

How can you as a parent ensure success for your child in the context of these new examinations? There will be some things that are vital and pressing for you to know and do.

1. You will need to know that, in most subjects, the practical and course work that your child will have been working on for two years, before the actual examination, will be assessed by the teacher and the marks sent to the examining board. These marks will form part of the overall examination mark in that subject. In some subjects, there will be no examinations at all, and the pupils will be assessed entirely on course work. This is called 'continuous assessment'. So it will be very important for your child to settle to work very seriously from the very beginning of the fourth year. You will want, therefore, to provide a settled environment for your child right from the beginning of their course.

2. You will need to know that during the fourth and fifth years a 'profile' – this kind of 'character cum personality' record which I have mentioned before – will be kept of your child. I feel that it is a document to which will be attached greater and greater importance as time goes on, and it could be asked for by any future employer or a principal of a college or university.

3. It will now be extremely important that you develop a good working partnership between yourself and your child's school. There should be as much personal contact as possible between yourself and the teaching staff so that no decisions are made about your child which you know nothing about. Make sure that no snap decisions are made about your youngster's personality. A shy child can often give the impression of being unfriendly and standoffish; a nervous child can give the impression of being insolent. But if you are in constant contact with the school, and attend all functions, you will be more and more able to help the teacher to tip the balance in favour of your child.

4. So that your child can sail calmly through all this and do justice to their many talents that previously would have remained untapped, always be prepared to ask and query, and delve and insist. Take queries to parents' evenings and open evenings and make personal appointments with whoever you need to see.

So, let me simplify and summarize the new GCSE examination for you in a question and answer form.

What is the GCSE?
The General Certificate of Secondary Education is the new single system of examinations at 16+.

These examinations replace GCE 'O' Level, CSE and Joint 'O' Level/CSE examinations.

What are the advantages of the GCSE?
The GCSE aims to help all pupils to do better. It will be fairer to pupils. All pupils will have the chance to show what they know, understand and can do.

How is the GCSE different?
(a) There is more emphasis on practical work and oral work.
(b) The courses will be relevant to pupils' experiences.
(c) Not everything will depend on the final examination.

How can the same examination be suitable for all pupils?
The GCSE is a single system of examination, with a single scale of grades. But pupils will not all do exactly the same classwork and examination questions. In the final examina-

tion in many subjects there will be a choice of papers or questions to suit pupils' abilities. So pupils can choose to give themselves the best chance to show what they can do.

What are the grades?
Successful pupils will be awarded a grade, on a single scale, from A to G.

Grades A to C will have standards at least as high as 'O' Level A to C and CSE grade 1.

'O' LEVEL	GCSE	CSE
A ⟷	A	
B ⟷	B	1
C ⟷	C	

Grades D to G will have standards at least as high as CSE grades 2 to 5.

GCSE	CSE
D ⟷	2
E ⟷	3
F ⟷	4
G ⟷	5

Candidates who do not reach the standards required for Grade G will not be given a result.

Part V
PROBLEMS IN AND OUT OF SCHOOL

Chapter 1.
Talking things through

Chapter 2.
Drugs

Chapter 3.
Solvent abuse

Chapter 4.
Smoking

Chapter 5.
Alcohol

Chapter 6.
Teenage sex and AIDS

CHAPTER 1
TALKING THINGS
THROUGH

When you've got teenagers, then you know you've got worries – because the teenage years are vulnerable ones. Adolescence can be a difficult time of mental and physical changes; of pressures at school; of enticement from friends; of increasingly complex types of temptation in an increasingly complicated world.

What can you do to protect your children, so that the good work you've embarked upon continues into this area as well? The answer is this:

1. You provide them with enough self-esteem, enough self-respect, not to need any props like drink or drugs

2. You bring them up to recognize that they are unique in their own right and have their own special role in the home, in school, and in society.

3. You love them for what they are and provide a secure home background against which to develop.

4. You take an interest in all their activities, not with an air of monitoring their whereabouts but because you find their pursuits interesting and worthwhile.

5. You demonstrate through your own conduct that there are some things which are acceptable and beneficial to do, and other things which are damaging and degrading.

6. You provide them with a good enough level of nutrients in their food so that there are no hidden hungers and cravings within the body to make them easy prey to addiction and abuse.

These things you have, as a concerned-parent, already done. You need to do one more thing: you need to discuss these problems with your child; you need to bring them out into the open and provide all the relevant facts about them. Educating and informing the child about dangers, in an atmosphere of care and concern, is the one sure way of reversing the dreadful tide of abuses and misuses that are rife in today's society.

Supposing you find it a bit awkward to broach these matters to your son or daughter? Many parents do, but one method that worked in our family was to casually address each other in front of the children. We would bring up the 'awkward' subject as part of a discussion that we'd heard in the staffroom. For instance when we wanted to discuss contraception my wife mentioned that in a friend's school half the third year girls were on the pill. Her casual manner brought a spontaneous response from our daughter and we began to talk about the whole subject.

The ice was broken; or, a better way of putting it would be to say that a pathway was cleared and it was possible for us all to discuss it together.

If you have no staff-room to draw upon, there is no harm in manufacturing a situation. You could say that during your visit to the dentist, or at a coffee-morning, you and an acquaintance had been discussing such and such a topic. Even if they're a bit imaginary at times you'll find it the easiest way of opening up a discussion.

CHAPTER 2
DRUGS

To parents, the most terrifying of all dangers are 'drugs'. They have visions of pushers at the school gate offering their child 'a taste', or concealing a taste in a harmless treat; they imagine a friend offering something which 'everyone takes for fun', and their youngster finds it too difficult to say no.

A growing number of children *are* finding it more difficult to say no, and, even though some will sooner or later drop the habit, a number will go on to develop a serious drug addiction.

Drugs, of course, can mean anything from smoking and alcohol to caffeine and aspirin, but when people mention drugs, they usually mean controlled drugs, the drugs which are used illegally, such as:

Heroin – known also as 'smack' and 'skag'.
Cannabis – known also as 'pot', 'dope', 'hash', 'grass'.
Cocaine – known also as 'coke'.
LSD – known also as 'acid'.
Amphetamine – known also as 'speed'.
Magic mushrooms –
Other opiates (painkillers) – known also as 'dikes', or '118's', and tranquillizers, which are prescribed tablets taken wrongfully for kicks, in combination with alcohol.

The one effect that all drug users are after is the euphoria that these drugs induce, the cushioning against reality. Tolerance for all drugs, too, happens very quickly, and therefore the addict requires more and more in order to experience the 'kicks', and more and more to counteract the horror of withdrawal.

A £100,000 drug education project was launched in

November 1986 by the Health Education Council, called Drug Wise. The project has involved five specialist agencies, and contains learning materials, a training manual, and a curriculum guide. The pack is aimed at helping youngsters to explore their attitudes and values, and to acquire skills such as assertiveness.

Is the school your child goes to using, or intending to use, this pack? Ask the Headteacher, or bring the matter up at a PTA meeting. Perhaps classes could be arranged where parents and youngsters could go along to discuss the problem together.

If you think your child may be dabbling with drugs then talk to the school and seek professional help immediately.

CHAPTER 3
SOLVENT ABUSE

The availability of products containing solvents – nail polish; glue; hairspray; typewriter correcting fluid; lighter fuel and many domestic cleaning substances – is very disturbing. In 1983, glue-sniffing accounted for 30 per cent of all solvent-related deaths and in 1986 research showed that 1 in 4 children had tried sniffing glue.

And solvents are just as harmful to a youngster as drugs; in fact, children of school age are more likely to be solvent abusers than drug abusers, because it's so cheap and easy to obtain, and no-one's breaking the law. The effect is very rapid. It causes sensations very similar to intoxication, except that it acts much more quickly than alcohol, because solvent is absorbed through the lungs rather than through the digestive tract. There is distention of vision, blurring of speech, aggression, hallucinations and eventual coma. Signs to look out for are scabs around the mouth; sore and runny nose, glazing over of the eyes, flushing of the face. Solvents could possibly also cause brain damage, since the chemicals in solvents are absorbed by fatty tissue, which includes the brain, and these chemicals are excreted at a very slow rate. Many sniffers concentrate the effect of the vapour from any solvent by placing a plastic bag over the head and inhaling from inside. Death from suffocation can result quite easily, as the reaction of the youngster is slower, apart from the fact that they could possibly have already entered into a coma.

An independent educational charity, called Re-Solv, has been established to support and advise anyone involved with solvent abusers. Their headquarters are in St Mary's Chambers, Stone, in Staffordshire. Together with the BASA – The British Adhesives and Sealants Association – they have produced guidelines for retailers, and stickers for display in shops, informing that the sale of products containing solvents may be refused to youngsters.

CHAPTER 4
SMOKING

'There are worrying signs for youngsters' health – 31% of boys leaving school and 28% of girl leavers, are regular smokers. Secondary school pupils spend around one-and-a-half million pounds on up to twenty-six million cigarettes a year.'

So claims the report: 'Social Trends', published by the Central Statistical Office on 29 January 1987.

Any teacher will tell you that stopping the number of children who take up smoking is a very difficult battle to wage.

If you spent some time in a secondary school, you would recognize that there are some very subtle persuaders which could cause a child to start the smoking habit within the set-up of the school itself. The staff-room, in some schools, huddles under a pall of smoke which drifts out of the door and can be smelled by any pupil approaching the staff-room corridor. Not many schools have any definite policy about smoking among its staff, but research has shown that teachers and parents who smoke in front of pupils exercise a bad influence.

Another insidious thing about the influence of schools in the development of the smoking habit is that, although most schools forbid younger children to smoke, they may allow the sixth formers to do so. Usually, what the sixth form do, the younger ones will want to emulate. Check that the school your child attends does not have a group of older indoctrinators, be they the sixth form pupils or the teachers, who might be the hidden persuaders in the process of developing the smoking habit in your child. Talk to the headteacher about the policy in his or her school.

Having bashed the teachers, parents as well are guilty of setting a bad example. Fine if you do not smoke, and fine even if the child sees you seriously trying to give up smoking. But even if you cannot possibly refrain from smoking try not to smoke in the child's presence if at all possible. Never offer a child a cigarette, and never send them to the shop to buy cigarettes if you've run out.

So why is it that so many youngsters start the smoking habit? Why is it, when our knowledge of the horrific effects of smoking has increased and is being relayed to school-children via lectures and films; when many public areas, like cinemas and restaurants, ban smoking that they still come under the smoking spell?

David Simpson, Director of Action on Smoking and Health (ASH), maintains that: 'Once children start looking forward to being "grown-up" and come under the influence of older teenagers, all common sense goes out of the window.' I quite agree. It's mostly pointless telling youngsters about the long-term dangers of smoking. It's better, I find, to stress the negative immediate results of smelly clothes, hair and breath, and yellow teeth.

The horror of lung cancer is far too far in the future to inspire any dread. Youngsters don't relate to the stark facts that the cigarette habit kills thousands of people every year in Britain, and millions world-wide. Not many are bothered that of all the children at school now, over half-a-million are likely to die, unnecessarily, from complaints brought on by cigarettes.

Nevertheless, such facts and statistics should be pointed out to children.

There are some very interesting observations by Griffith Edwards, a Professor of Addictive Behaviour at London University.

'It does appear that those children having trouble with their work are more likely to start smoking than those who are more confident. If parents and teachers can recognize the problem, they may stop a child turning to artificial stimuli like cigarettes.'

It all boils down, again, to self-esteem, to the value a child places on themselves and their own well-being; and the immeasurable benefits of being successful at school work. As a caring parent, you know how to ensure the certainty of this.

CHAPTER 5
ALCOHOL

When we celebrate a special occasion or anniversary; when we relax with friends; at parties; to clinch a business deal; we turn to this pleasant-looking, pleasant-tasting drink, whose initial effect is also pleasant, making the drinker more relaxed and confident. But alcoholic drink is a two-faced monster – it is also potentially lethal, extremely dangerous, and possible to get addicted to. It can destroy relationships, self-respect, health, caution, and financial and emotional stability. It destroys the body and it destroys the mind. Particularly vulnerable are the liver, the heart, the stomach, the unborn child, and the cells of the brain.

Drinking in excess is far more serious and far more widespread than glue-sniffing and hard drugs. It causes the deaths in Britain of a thousand times as many people as heroin.

1. Alcohol abuse costs the country around £1,700 million every year for accidents associated with alcohol; absentee-ism from work, and many other social problems associated with alcohol.

2. A third of all road accidents are caused by drivers under the influence of alcohol, and half of all the accidents which occur in the home are due to drink.

3. In 1984, 80 per cent of 13-year-olds said that they had had an alcoholic drink, according to 'Social Trends'. Mrs Ticka Levonem of AAA reports an increase in under-age drinking, and that the majority of children are drinking at the age of fifteen.

4. Some children drink more than 50 pints of beer a week –
in pubs where many landlords turn a blind eye.

Under-age drinking among the under eighteens – and heavy
drinking occurs almost evenly in girls as in boys – is a
problem that is growing more and more serious. Teachers,
more than any group in society, recognize the extent of the
problem. It's getting quite a common occurrence now for
pupils in upper forms of secondary schools to be sent home
for being drunk after a bout of lunchtime drinking. More and
more schools are requesting information about drink and
teachers are openly admitting that the volume of under-age
drinking is becoming truly frightening.

Young people should be given information about the
horrific effects of alcohol abuse. They need advice about how
much alcohol is too much; how alcohol affects the body; and
what happens when people mix different drinks. They need
to know that alcohol affects a small person more than
someone of larger size, and that it can stay in the
bloodstream for many hours after actually drinking. They
need to know that alcohol clouds judgement and slows
down reactions, so that doing anything requiring skill after
drinking – operating any machine; riding a bike; driving a
car; even swimming – is best avoided. They need to know
that alcohol is the prime cause of criminal offences amongst
youngsters, and that road accidents after drinking is the
biggest cause of death amongst young men.

Many such facts as these are available in an excellent
leaflet called *That's The Limit*, published by the Health
Education Council. You can obtain it free from PO Box 420,
London, SE99 6YE, and I recommend it for all teenagers.

From discussing drinking problems with many youngsters, it seems that the reason most of them drink is because
their friends drink. They wish to appear daring and adult
and they regard getting drunk as perfectly acceptable. So
one of the most important things to stress upon a youngster
is that it's not chicken or soft to say no when offered an
alcoholic drink and claim preference for a soft drink. I'm no
believer in soft drinks and colas, but in this context, to ask for
a coke could keep a youngster alive, or certainly out of
serious trouble.

So what do you need to instil into your youngsters so that

they are well armed whenever they go anywhere near alcohol?

1. Keep stressing never to be afraid of refusing a drink, that it's neither clever nor wise to accept alcohol.

2. If your child is going to a party, tell them not to drink on an empty stomach, and never to mix drinks.

3. Tell them never to drive any machine or vehicle after drinking, and never to accept a lift from anyone who's been drinking.

No harm will come to your youngster if, over the years, you have built up their self-esteem, and if they feel adequate in their own right; if they know that you care and they feel secure as an individual. If you have treated your child positively: giving praise instead of criticism; encouraging and supporting them to take responsibility, then they will make positive decisions. If you've always treated them as an adult, and always pointed out that actions have certain consequences then they will be able to make the adult decisions about avoiding all the temptations that will come their way. You can't supervise them all the time, but you will have given the tools to enable them to supervise their own well-being.

CHAPTER 6
TEENAGE SEX AND AIDS

Today, more and more youngsters are sexually active in their early and mid-teens. It seems that a sexual relationship is the passport to respect amongst peers, and many youngsters consider themselves 'out of it' if they don't have a sexual relationship. What they see on television is no help; there are very conflicting messages conveyed through films and television. The characters meet, fall in love, and sleep with each other – within five minutes. It's no wonder kids think they're nobody if they don't have sex.

As the average age for sexual activity gets younger and younger, so doctors, teachers, and youth workers are getting more and more worried because the dangers of teenage sex are both physical and emotional.

For a start, there are such conditions as pelvic inflammatory disease, an infection of the fallopian tubes which is increasing in young girls; it is mostly sexually transmitted and can result in infertility. There's gonorrhoea and chlamydia; there are genital warts that can lead to cancer; and there's the proven fact that sexually active teenage girls are at greater risk of developing cancer of the cervix when they become adults.

Apart from the medical undesirability of early sex, there is the emotional aspect. Youngsters are not ready, emotionally, for a sexual relationship when they're in their mid-teens. When young people engage in sexual activity at too early an age, they are more likely to become involved, later in life, in relationships that are based purely on sex, with tragic consequences because they are not usually loving and caring relationships.

I think there is a world of sense in an earlier rather than

later approach to sex education. Start talking to your own children about sex and the facts of life when they're around five, or six, or seven. There is no embarrassment at this stage, and having been used to talking to them about sex, there will be no embarrassment at a later stage.

The majority of us want our children to grow up with a sane and healthy attitude towards all sexual matters. The best way of ensuring this is for the parent to have a sane and healthy attitude towards sex. If the child is fortunate enough to be brought up by parents who demonstrate love and care and consideration, then this is the most valuable and certain 'programming' the youngster could possibly get.

By all means check that they know about such things as venereal disease, contraception, the process of conception and about reproduction and birth. But try to instil the 'ideals' as well.

Ask your youngster's head-teacher what line his or her school takes in sex education. If their answer is a bit nebulous and if you get the impression that teaching in this area is a bit fragmentary, plead for a more co-ordinated approach. Re-enforcement by the school of what is taught at home will make certain that your youngster is put on the right tracks.

AIDS

All of Britain's twenty-three million households have now received the leaflet *AIDS – Don't Die of Ignorance*. Make certain that your daugher or your son reads the pamphlet, over and over, unless of course they're too young. Make certain you discuss it with your youngster and make certain that they understand exactly how AIDS can be caught. The government's message is, for most adults, simple, explicit and clear, except that various terms such as semen, lubricating gel, acupuncture or blood transfusions would not be understood by all youngsters in their early or mid teens. Make certain that these terms are understood, however little you relish the task of explaining.

Make certain that your youngster understands that this is a world-wide killer epidemic, without a historical precedent and that millions of people around the world risk death from AIDS.

INDEX

About the author

Gwilym Roberts, B.Sc., Dip.I.O.N., graduated in Science at the University College of North Wales, Bangor, and then spent his post-graduate year training to be a teacher, a profession he had wanted to follow from a very early age. In his first teaching post abroad, he taught physics and mathematics to British Service children. He has taught in a variety of schools, gaining experience with children of all abilities and from a wide range of backgrounds.

For the past fifteen years, he has been Head of the Science Department at Darland School, Rossett, North Wales, and has developed a department known for its academic excellence and success. There is nothing that Mr Roberts enjoys more than witnessing the success of the pupils in whom he takes a great personal and professional interest.

In these past few years, he has developed an interest in healthy eating and has been furthering his studies with the Institute for Optimum Nutrition, London. He feels that nutrition is a major factor in influencing the behaviour and academic performance of children. His recent nutrition trial with pupils at Darland School, indicated a link between success at school and optimum nutrition, and gained him national publicity.

Gwilym Roberts lives in North Wales with his wife, and both teach part-time as well as run an Education and Nutrition Consultancy. Both his daughters are married with young children, and his son is a student.

0896 111 081
01666 505 669